What Expert Teachers Say About Teaching Mathematics
Grades K–8

A Resource and Discussion Book for Preservice and Inservice Teachers

RICHARD DAHLKE
ROGER VERHEY
University of Michigan–Dearborn

DALE SEYMOUR PUBLICATIONS

ISBN 0-86651-308-6
Order number DS01609

DALE
SEYMOUR
PUBLICATIONS
P.O. BOX 10888
PALO ALTO, CA 94303

bcdefghi-MA-8932109

Preface

The primary purpose of this book is to give preservice and in-service teachers of K–8 mathematics insights into how expert teachers manage their teaching of elementary or middle school mathematics. The book is also intended as a catalyst for stimulating discussion on the management of mathematics instruction.

The book is based on *questions* covering 34 different topics related to the teaching of mathematics and includes carefully selected *responses* from experienced teachers. Following every set of responses are *exercises* that help readers focus their thinking on the preceding question and on related issues. Although the emphasis is on mathematics, many of the questions, responses, and exercises are applicable to the teaching of most subjects.

For *preservice K–8 teachers*, the book will be of assistance in the *initial development* of an effective management plan for their teaching of mathematics. It can be used in a mathematics methods course, a general methods or teaching strategies course, or a mathematics content course. It can also be used individually as a resource manual.

For *inservice teachers*, the book can be a stimulus for *considering changes* in their management plans for teaching mathematics. It can provide the focus for an inservice program or workshop, and it can also be used individually as a resource manual.

How This Book Came About

This book is the culmination of mathematics education project that grew out of a more informal project. The original pilot project was conducted by one of the authors in response to the practical class management concerns of preservice teachers enrolled in his mathematics laboratory course. Together the class and instructor drew up a set of questions about how to manage the teaching of K–8 mathematics and asked experienced teachers to respond to the resulting questionnaire. Those teacher responses were then screened and edited for inclusion in the pilot booklet.

We used the pilot booklet for four years to stimulate student discussion in our mathematics content and mathematics education courses. The positive reactions of our students to that booklet encouraged us to repeat the project, but with improvements in the questionnaire and in the selection of teachers asked to complete it. To help with these changes, we formed an advisory committee of leading mathematics educators from southeastern Michigan (see listing on page x).

In making the selection of teachers, the advisory committee either chose teachers they personally viewed as being excellent in the teaching of mathematics, or they contacted school principals and asked them to help make the choice. For a list of the participating teachers, see page xi.

After receiving the completed questionnaires, we began the task of reviewing them. In particular, we looked for responses that suggested useful management techniques or provided other information that would be valuable for discussion purposes. We also reviewed the responses to our pilot questionnaire and included some of the best in this book. It became increasingly clear to us, as we were selecting and editing responses, that exercises to stimulate thought and discussion would help involve the reader in using the ideas in this book. Thus we added a set of exercises for each item on our questionnaire.

How This Book Is Organized

The table of contents includes the full text of each numbered question, enabling the reader to locate the discussion of particular issues. In a few instances, closely related questions are identified by the same number; for example, the five questions that relate to the grouping of students in a class are identified as 16a through 16e.

Since most aspects of teaching mathematics are interrelated, responses to one question often contained information that would form an equally suitable response to another question. Thus, when seeking information about a particular teaching concern, the reader is encouraged to look through the table of contents, note all the questions that seem to be related, and then read the associated responses.

Turn to the opening page for any question and you will see the format used for the teacher responses. The number in parentheses preceding each individual response is a code for that particular respondent. A respondent carries this code throughout the book; hence, all of that teacher's responses that we included can be readily located. You may find it advantageous to read all the selected responses for a particular respondent. For example, you might want to read all the remarks of Teachers 4 and 17, who have the most responses in the book. If the ideas of a particular teacher appeal to you, we encourage you to look for other responses from this same person.

Each response is followed by a phrase indicating the grade level or levels that the respondent was teaching at the time the questionnaire was completed. Since we feel that much can be gained by reading *all* the responses to a question, we did not group responses according to grade levels. Primary, intermediate, and middle school teachers have important things to say to each other on the teaching of mathematics, as the reader will discover in these pages.

At the end of each set of teacher responses you will find the exercises for that question. While these can be assigned as written work, it is our intent that they be used primarily as a basis for group discussions. In most instances, a set of exercises will also include one or two *projects* that refer the reader to outside sources. These projects are generally more meaningful and practical for the preservice teacher than for the inservice teacher. However, many of the reading sources referred to can be of significant benefit to inservice teachers as well, and they are encouraged to seek them out. Sometimes when a source is mentioned, it is followed by a number in parentheses. This number is keyed to our annotated bibliography (see page 153).

Individual Use of This Book

There are many ways to use this book on your own. One way is to select a question from the table of contents and think about what your answer would be. Then read the responses to that question and summarize, preferably on paper, what the teacher respondents have said. Follow this by responding once more to the question yourself. Also read the exercises, respond to those that interest you, and do some of the readings suggested in the projects. We encourage you to share with a colleague or fellow student any thoughts and concerns that arise from doing these activities.

The book can also be useful when a specific management problem arises in your teaching of mathematics. In this case, turn to the table of contents to see if any of the questions address your problem. If so, you should find some ideas on handling this problem among the responses to those questions.

A note of caution: If you are a teacher and want to make some improvements in your teaching, realize that changing well-established habits must be done gradually. Don't try changing too many things at once lest you become discouraged and abandon your goal to make improvements.

Using the Book for Inservice Training

We have designed two possible plans for a workshop using this book. Certain variables, including the time available for the workshop, will dictate what changes might have to be made in each plan.

The first plan assumes that teachers will be asked to do some preparation for the workshop. Each teacher should be asked to select and rank three questions from the table of contents that most interest them. Based on this information, the workshop leader should select the best questions and exercises for discussion. The teachers should then be asked to read the responses to those questions *before* coming to the workshop and also to think about what their own responses would be.

On the day of the workshop, the leader should begin with a whole-group discussion of one of the chosen questions and its related exercises. This serves as a model for the small-group discussions that will follow. Each small group that is formed will be assigned one or more of the remaining questions and related exercises. In the final hour of the workshop, each small group summarizes their discussion for the whole group. If time permits, participants can bring up any questions or comments about the small-group reports or about related issues.

In closing the workshop, the leader should encourage participants to have periodic meetings with their teaching colleagues throughout the school year to discuss other questions that appear in this book. Thus, in a natural way, concerns involving the teaching of mathematics and the mathematics curriculum will surface for debate. The workshop leader should also encourage the participants to read some of the articles referred to in the projects. In particular, *Research Within Reach: Elementary School Mathematics* (1) should be mentioned.

The second plan assumes that teachers will not be asked to do any work ahead of time. At the outset of the workshop, the inservice leader should familiarize the participants with this book by mentioning how it came about, describing its main elements, and presenting the table of contents. Then one of the questions could be posed to the participants. Following a discussion of the question, the participants should read the responses given in the book. There should then be time for further discussion based on the reading and on the related exercises. A second question of interest might then be picked for general discussion. The remainder of the workshop can be structured, as in the first plan, with small-group discussions of other questions that are of particular interest to the participants.

Using the Book with Preservice Teachers

There is a wide range of possibilities for using this book in preservice courses. The instructor may want to expose the students to just a few of the ideas in these pages so they will leave the course with an understanding of what's in the book and how they can use it. Or, the instructor may want to use the book rather extensively throughout the course, in which case students will leave the course with many good ideas on managing the teaching of mathematics.

The book can be introduced in one class period. One possible approach is as follows: The instructor begins the period with an overview of the table of contents, then selects one question and asks each student to write a response. This is followed immediately by a class discussion of the students' answers. Students should then read and discuss what the teacher respondents had to say on this question. As a homework assignment, the students write a second response to the same question. During the next class period students are asked to share both their initial and final responses. The purpose here is to impress upon students that consolidating the information they gain from reading *and* from carrying on discussions with their classmates will better prepare them to manage the teaching of mathematics. They should also be aware of the importance of continuing to discuss issues with colleagues when they are teaching.

As follow-up homework, the instructor might assign some of the exercises associated with the question that was used for the initial work. Again, the greatest benefit derives from having the students *talk about* their responses. The value of discussion cannot be overestimated; both whole-group and small-group discussion should be a continual part of students' work with this book. On occasion students should work on the assignments in small groups outside of class. This will leave more time during class for whole-group discussion. Related issues will definitely surface as a result of the homework, and there must be time to address these.

Longer-term projects could also be assigned to individuals or groups. For example, an instructor might ask students to do weekly, monthly, or semester projects based on certain exercises from the book.

It is unwise and perhaps not even possible to discuss in a single course all the questions and exercises that appear in this book. There is far too much information to do an adequate job with each one. Thus, it is important for the instructor to take care in choosing which questions and exercises to use for class and individual work. What is most important is to spend enough time with the book in class so that students learn what is in it. They should see how they might tackle a particular teaching concern through reading and discussion, and then come up with a viable management idea they can act on.

Other Resources

The source we most often refer to in this book is *Research Within Reach: Elementary School Mathematics* (1). This is an excellent and very readable book, written for preservice and inservice teachers, that complements our book well. We highly recommend that it be used concurrently with *What Expert Teachers Say About Teaching Mathematics (Grades K–8)*.

It is not possible to list all the excellent materials that are now available to teachers for their professional libraries or for use with their students. We have included a few of the very best in our annotated bibliography (see page 153).

A number of teacher respondents refer throughout our book to CSMP, the Comprehensive School Mathematics Program (3). See the bibliography for further information on this program.

Appreciation

We wish to express our deep appreciation to our advisory committee and to the teachers who participated in this project.

Dedication

We dedicate this project to our parents, Victor and Joan Dahlke and Richard and Catherine Verhey. We are proud that both couples recently celebrated their golden wedding anniversaries.

R. D.
R. V.

Advisory Committee

Dr. Rita Brey
Detroit Public Schools

Dr. Alfred Capoferi
Macomb County Intermediate School District

Dr. Theresa Denman
Detroit Public Schools

Ms. Margie Farrand
Ann Arbor Public Schools

Dr. Geraldine Green
Royal Oak Public Schools

Ms. Rande Neugent
St. Clair Shores Public Schools

Dr. Albert Shulte
Oakland County Intermediate School District

Dr. Marie Vitale
Ann Arbor Public Schools

Teacher Respondents

George Allen
Busch Middle School
Centerline Public School District

Beverly Aronwits
Chaney Elementary School
Detroit Public School District

Donna Bialach
Washington Elementary School
Ferndale School District

Ruth Boyd
Washington Junior High School
Pontiac City School District

Jean E. Campbell
Taft Elementary School
Ferndale School District

Robert E. Cox
Pine Lake Elementary School
Bloomfield Hills School District

Lynn Cronin
Einstein Elementary School
Fraser Public School District

Paula Cruickshank
Switzer Elementary School
Utica Coummunity School District

Kay Dittmer
Shorewood Elementary School
Lake Shore School District

Maude Donahue
Roosevelt School
Ferndale School District

Elaine Drutchas
Booth Elementary School
Bloomfield Hills School District

Lee Ann Duggan
Cass Elementary School
Livonia School District

Joseph Foster
John Page Middle School
Lamphere Public School District

Jane Frank
Scarlett Junior High School
Ann Arbor Public School District

Patricia E. Geister
Wines Elementary School
Ann Arbor Public School District

Beverly Good
Hoover Elementary School
Livonia School District

Patricia Gosik
Westwood Elementary School
Warren Woods School District

Dennys Grady
Andrew Jackson Elementary School
Ferndale School District

Robert Hage
Wass Elementary School
Troy School District

Gloria Haynes
Switzer Elementary School
Utica Community School District

Carol Hermann
Smith Middle School
Troy School District

Charles E. Johnston
Roosevelt Elementary School
Livonia School District

Anne Kloack
Allen Elementary School
Ann Arbor Public School District

Evelyn Konz
Crary Elementary School
Detroit Public School District

Caroline Kracht
Pare Elementary School
South Lake School District

Patricia Larson
Andrew Jackson Elementary School
Ferndale School District

Judy Lewandowski
Flynn Junior High School
Warren Consolidated School District

Phyllis Lewandowski
Page Middle School
Lamphere Public School District

Elaine Lowenthal
Stratford Elementary School
Detroit Public School District

Elaine J. McAfee
Dean A. Naldrett Elementary School
Anchor Bay School District

Elizabeth McMurrough
North Elementary School
Warren Consolidated School District

Jane Maulbetsch
Scarlett Junior High School
Ann Arbor Public School District

Jeannette Medlyn
Larned Elementary School
Detroit Public School District

Lynda Neuroth
Collidge Elementary School
Livonia School District

Geraldine I. Nowak
Burton International School
Detroit Public School District

Ann G. Oklejas
Harding Elementary School
Ferndale School District

Nancy Poulin
Lakewood Elementary School
Ann Arbor Public School District

Gail Reichmann
Fillmore Elementary School
Warren Consolidated School District

Sally Reid
Chesterfield Elementary School
L'Anse Creuse School District

Sandra A. Richards
Jack Harvey Elementary School
Utica Community School District

Bonnie Robb
Westview Elementary School
Fitzgerald School District

Barbara L. Robinson
Haisley Elementary School
Ann Arbor Public School District

Peg Sanok
Bellview Elementary School
East Detroit School District

Beverly Schimmelpfennig
Chatterton Middle School
Fitzgerald School District

Karren Schneider
Will L. Lee Elementary School
Richmond Community School District

Ernest A. Sciullo
Flynn Junior High School
Warren Consolidated School District

Judy Z. Somers
Forsythe Junior High School
Ann Arbor Public School District

Linda S. Somers
Washington Elementary School
Ferndale School District

Beverly Spector
Harding Elementary School
Ferndale School District

Gloria Stein
Lawton Elementary School
Ann Arbor Public School District

Michael J. Tucker
Bell Elementary School
Detroit Public School District

Sharon F. Vagi
Gruebner Elementary School
Utica Community School District

Linda Wade
Franklin Elementary School
Royal Oak Public School District

Esther Williams
Hayes Elementary School
Livonia School District

Karen M. Wilson
Armada Elementary School
Armada Area School District

Christine Zakalata-Blakemore
MacCulloch Elementary School
Detroit Public School District

Contents

Maintaining Skills

Developing Problem-Solving Skills

Using Manipulative Aids

Using the Textbook

Using Workbooks

Using Reproducible Materials

Working a Lesson Without Teacher Explanation

Keeping and Using Mathematical Records

Evaluating a Student's Math Knowledge

Sources for Written Tests

Assignments

Grouping Students

Not Grouping Students

Helping Students Who Lack Prerequisites

Providing for the Academically Talented

Providing for the Academically Deficient

Providing for the Mainstreamed Student

Special Resource Materials

Finding Time to Give Individual Help

Students Helping Other Students

Teacher Aides and Volunteer Helpers

Involving Parents in Helping Their Children

Sources for Alternative Teaching Strategies

Students' Making Up Work

Techniques for Motivating Students

Relating Math to the Real World

District's Policy on Length of Math Period

Time of Class Period

Allotting Class Time

Miscellaneous Comments on Math Teaching

Determining Content

Question 1: What besides the textbook helps you determine the mathematical content you will cover for the school year?

Teacher Responses

(2) At the beginning of the school year, I test for first grade readiness in recognizing and writing sets and numbers, matching objects, counting, quantity and position words, classifying, and patterning. Student readiness in these areas helps determine the teaching content in addition to the basic textbook. *(Grade 1)*

(3) For several years I have been amazed at how much money children have to spend (grades four and five), and how little they are able to relate to the real world of cost, coupons and rebates, sales tax, and hourly wages. Since our textbook currently in use does little with consumer math, I have used a math period every now and then to develop an awareness of cost of grocery items, toys and games, clothing, school supplies, bicycles, and stereos. November and December are good times to use catalogs and Sunday paper advertising for

lesson material. Interest runs high! *Penny Power* magazine is helpful as a high interest resource for a consumer math lesson. *(Grades 4-5)*

(4) I check kindergarten records to see what concepts were introduced and what concepts were mastered. I conduct a quick screening to find children who are weak in some basic concepts and then make these concepts a part of our program. Since our science program includes comparison properties (or attributes), and also the concepts of greater than and less than, I incorporate these into the math program too. I also do some cooking with the children during the year, and this determines how much we go into fractions. I also include topics that our first grade math text does not cover. (Some of these were in the former edition of the text.) Such topics are missing addends, number sequence (before, between, and after), number names (the words one, two, three, etc.), geoboards, tangrams, symmetry, and tetrominoes. *(Grade 1)*

(8) The district has outlined minimal math objectives for each grade level. I cover these as well as topics in the book. In addition, I teach math skills that are needed for studies of other subjects such as science and social studies. Also, I look for math topics to use for enrichment, weekly problem-solving activities, and extension of the normal course work. *(Grades 3-4)*

(17) The content of the mathematics program in my classroom is influenced by many considerations:

1. The content of the Big Three exams: the Metropolitan Achievement, the seventh grade Michigan Assessment, and our school district's criterion-referenced test.
2. The students' knowledge of various math concepts when they enter my classroom in September, which is evaluated through an oral speed quiz on all basic facts, through the tests put out by the textbook publisher, and through my own tests, which always include a quantity of "zero-type" problems. Correct answers on the latter problems usually indicate to me the mastery of a concept.
3. The students' ability to absorb and retain concepts, exhibited during the first several weeks of the school year.
4. The students' own enthusiasm and interest in math and math-related topics. I may try hard, but I can't do it all alone.

5. My own personal enthusiasm and interest in math, which leads me to supervise noon recess computer instruction and to sponsor a fifth and sixth grade Equations gaming club with several Saturday tournaments. I make time for extra math instruction.

6. My meetings with junior high math teachers every three to four years. Our discussions include weak areas they see among entering seventh grade students.

7. The math strengths and weaknesses witnessed among my own four sons, from a history major to an engineering major. Some are directly attributable to strengths and weaknesses of early experiences at home and school.

8. The needs of society. It seems that our present technological society can much better absorb math and science majors than it can, say, language-oriented graduates. This has increased my emphasis on math in the classroom. Every spare bit of wall space holds a poster board of some mathematical idea I can refer to with the class or individual student.
(Grade 6)

(18) During the past five years, our district has had a coordinated mathematics curriculum. The middle school math department heads and teachers have outlined a grades six through eight course of study and written corresponding essential objectives as well as test items. These objectives are to be covered by all students during the appropriate grade. Material covered beyond those objectives is at the teacher's discretion, with most teachers emphasizing material that is either needed by the student or interesting to the student or teacher. *(Grades 7-8)*

(28) I make periodic contacts with senior high teachers to determine weak areas in our junior high curriculum. Based on their suggestions, I've supplemented the curriculum with my own units, especially in story problems. Finally, the students' interest in calculators has led me to make use of them in the curriculum. *(Grades 7-8)*

(35) Hearing and reading what other people outside of education feel students need in math has helped me with innovations for students. Also, I have strong feelings that students need to be able to handle everyday math such as banking, budgeting, spending, etc. *(Grade 6)*

(36) We are using the CSMP elementary school program. The publishers provide a master schedule, which we follow. Some important topics are not included in CSMP so I provide additional instruction in those areas. So far this year we have had extra work in time, money, reading graphs, and additional drill and practice in basic math facts. These topics are taught on adjustment days in the CSMP schedule. *(Grade 3)*

(45) Since the Michigan Assessment Test and California Arithmetic Test are used each year to test students, the skills being tested must be taught, ideally, well in advance of the testing period. A good teacher helps prepare the students by incorporating tested skills into regular daily lessons. Publications such as the *Arithmetic Teacher* provide timely articles on the direction (i.e., most needed skills, timely topics, etc.) in which mathematics education should be moving. Pretesting at the beginning of the school year on grade-level skills for the previous year's work allows the teacher to focus on weaknesses of individuals and to provide them with an educational program to insure a year's growth. Class composition (i.e., accelerated students, immature students, disadvantaged students, etc.) also determines needed skills and realistic academic goals. *(Grades 3-4)*

(60) The content to be covered is determined by our district's mathematics committee in the sense that they decide which textbook will be used. The building department chairperson decides with the teachers which chapters will be covered. Student levels affect the time spent on each topic. *(Grades 7-8)*

Exercises for Question 1

1. List what the respondents use, besides the textbook, to determine the math content that they will cover for the school year. Can you add to this list? Which four items on your list do you view as most important?

2. Teachers 2, 4, 17, and 45 check for readiness content at the beginning of the school year and then plan their content for the school year accordingly. Is it best to determine readiness content at the beginning of the school year as opposed to determining this periodically during the school year? Explain.

3. Teachers 17 and 45 use the results of state or national assessment tests to help them determine the math content they will cover. What influence should these types of tests have on math content? Explain. What are some harmful effects of school districts placing too much pressure on teachers to get their students to perform well on these tests?

4. Teachers 17 and 28 seek advice from teachers at higher grade levels on the math concepts and skills that need to be included or stressed in their math classes. What advantages and disadvantages are there in doing this? What can a school district do to foster this? What can you do to foster this?

5. Discuss the advantages and disadvantages of using each of the following methods to determine the math content that is to be covered: the textbook (see response of Teacher 60); construction of objectives that are keyed to the text; construction of objectives that are not keyed to the text, with the material needed to meet all the objectives not being provided (see response of Teacher 8).

6. **Project.** One teacher, whose response to Question 1 was not included, stated that the NCTM booklet *An Agenda for Action: Recommendations for School Mathematics of the 1980s* (2c) had a profound influence on her planning of math content for the past two years. Write an overview of this publication.

7. **Project.** Read the bulletin "The Teacher and the Textbook" in *Research Within Reach: Elementary School Mathematics* (1) and write a summary of its content. Do you agree with its conclusion? Explain.

Ordering Concepts and Skills

Question 2:　How do you decide upon the order in which mathematical concepts or skills are to be presented?

Teacher Responses

(3)　I find the order of skills presented in the textbook to be in harmony with the developmental level of most students. The one exception to the book order, from which I digress, is the geometry unit. I like to teach some geometry lessons using geoboards earlier, around the middle of December, to offer variety and to lay the foundation for later geometric concepts involving lines and shapes. Solid shapes are also introduced out of textbook sequence so I can tie them in with an art lesson on showing perspective and three dimensionality. Another reason for planning a geometry unit at this time is that I often have extra children from another class; sometimes another grade is in my care due to schedule jostling for Christmas play rehearsals, etc. This kind of flexible programming spans grade levels and children respond well to variety at this time. At other times when I feel that children need a break from the regular routine, I will have several lessons using *TANGRAMATH. (Grades 4-5)*

(4)   I mostly follow the text. I might do "greater than" or "less than" at a little different point in the year so it coincides with our science program. The same could happen with the fractions module if we are cooking. *(Grade 1)*

(11)   Initially, math consists of reviewing and reinforcing the previous year's (second grade) math. Tests then are administered to identify on-grade and below-grade level students. Multiplication is introduced early in the year as most students require the full year to learn the tables. (It appears too late in the textbook.) Multiplication becomes a daily, year-long activity. Generally speaking, I follow the textbook order. *(Grade 3)*

(12)   I use our district's math objectives as a guide for sequence. I assess each child's skill level and move ahead from the last skill mastered. *(Grade 1)*

(28)   I have had the pleasure of teaching math from fifth grade up to ninth grade. You develop an inner resource or reference book in your mind. No matter what text you use, this "resource" reminds you that you can only cover a certain topic properly if you touch on a specific set of ideas in a certain order. For example, suppose the seventh grade text is ready to cover subtraction of fractions. As I prepare to write my lesson plans, I know I must cover the following skills in this order:
1.   Subtracting proper fractions with like denominators.
2.   Subtracting proper fractions with unlike denominators.
3.   Subtracting mixed numerals with like denominators.
4.   Subtracting mixed numerals with unlike denominators.
5.   Subtracting mixed numerals that require borrowing.
(Grades 7-8)

(31)   The order in which I present concepts has evolved through the years. The order in which the concepts are presented in the textbook has some bearing, but I do not allow it to dictate my program. For instance, I feel that I am most successful when I present fractions, decimals, and then metric measurement. Both measurement units in my basic text come before fractions and decimals are presented. One might say trial and error has helped me determine my basic outline. If I have difficulty getting a concept across to the children, I reconsider my ordering of concepts or skills as well as other ways of presenting them. *(Grade 4)*

Exercises for Question 2

1. Write a brief report, based on the responses and on your ideas, of when it seems reasonable to deviate from the order in which the textbook presents concepts and skills.

2. How important is it for a teacher to review with his or her students the sequencing of the mathematics content? Explain. When are good times to do this?

3. What are the advantages and disadvantages of teaching a math concept out of order because it is a necessary part of another area of the curriculum, like science, that is currently being studied? (See response of Teacher 4.)

4. **Project.** Write a summary of the bulletin "Sequence with Substance: The Elementary School Mathematics Curriculum" from *Research Within Reach: Elementary School Mathematics* (1).

5. **Project.** Read the article "A Teaching Sequence from Initial Fraction Concepts Through the Addition of Unlike Fractions" by Ellerbruch and Payne in the 1978 NCTM Yearbook *Developing Computational Skills* (2b). What specific statements about sequencing the teaching of fractions were most significant to you?

Omitting Topics

Question 3:   How do you decide which topics to omit?

Teacher Responses

(16) While I do not eliminate elements of the district's prescribed content, I may well eliminate sections of a text related to a specific topic if it appears to me that they will be confusing or unnecessarily cumbersome to my students. It seems logical, for instance, to work toward a simple basic understanding of a concept or operation rather than attempt to introduce six ways of doing the same thing and confuse the students in the process. *(Grade 6)*

(18) The topics to be omitted are done so with several questions in mind:
1. Is the topic taught in another course or at another level and therefore can be omitted if need be (e.g., metrics)?
2. Can the material be taught within the context of another unit? (For example, whole number work in eighth grade that is related to decimals can be taught in the decimal unit.)
3. Is the material really appropriate or essential to the students at this level?
(Grades 7-8)

(28)   It is extremely useful to be able to teach or to have taught courses in a sequence. This way you know what was covered in the previous course and likewise you know what fundamentals are required, and therefore must be stressed, so your students can succeed in the following course. If you are not so fortunate, then good communication between department members is crucial. Checking quarterly on how the students you've sent on are doing is important. Maybe in an effort to cover too much ground you have poorly prepared your students. Therefore, it is important the following year to delete material that unduly interferes with your teaching of material that is fundamental to your students' success in the next course. Needless to say, you can always return to these topics at the end of the year if time allows. *(Grades 7-8)*

(31)   I do not consciously think about what I can omit from my program. Rather, I think in terms of what I need to teach and to whom. In heterogeneous groupings there are always children who can far surpass the basic fourth grade requirements while others struggle to get the basic computational skills. *(Grade 4)*

(40)   I seldom omit topics presented in the text; but, if I feel the activity or topic is not appropriate to my group, I will either change it or leave it out. Perhaps they have already mastered the skill, the lesson may be poorly written, or the concept being taught is too difficult for them at this time. *(Grade 2)*

Exercises for Question 3

1.   It is safe to say that a major goal of any mathematics course is to prepare the students to succeed in a subsequent mathematics course. Teacher 28 mentions the importance of teaching mathematics courses in a sequence to know what your students have covered and will be covering. Do you view it important for a teacher to teach third and fifth grade occasionally if the teacher is basically a fourth grade teacher? Explain. Should a school system encourage this?

2.   In deciding which topics to omit, Teacher 31 thinks in terms of what needs to be taught and to whom. This suggests that some

topics may possibly be omitted for the class in general, but might be of interest to high-achieving students or be of value to low-achieving students. Would you omit or have you omitted topics on this basis? Explain.

3. Teacher 18 suggests that a topic might be omitted, if need be, if it is taught at another grade level. Will this cause a problem if the teacher at the higher grade level assumes that it has been taught and therefore only intends to review the topic? Explain.

4. Teacher 16 implies that some textbooks attempt to get at certain concepts or operations in more than one way and that this can be troublesome for students. On the other hand, there are good reasons for a textbook to present more than one model of a concept. For example, textbooks present the concept of subtraction of whole numbers using the models of "take-away" and "missing addend." Why is it important to present both subtraction models? Under what circumstances would you agree with Teacher 16?

5. What criteria would you use to omit a topic when pressured for time?

6. What are more appropriate paths for a teacher to follow than omitting content because it is in an area in which the teacher feels insecure? Can you name math content areas that are frequently omitted because of a teacher's insecurity?

7. **Project.** Consult a mathematics textbook for a particular grade and from each of two chapters in the first half of the book select a section that you would omit because of lack of time. Make copies of the sections to be deleted and give reasons that support these deletions.

Introducing a Concept or Skill

Question 4: What techniques have you found successful in introducing a concept or skill?

Teacher Responses

(2) I find pictures, manipulative materials, chalkboard demonstrations and classroom discussion based on children's experiences meaningful in introducing a concept or skill. Children are eager to learn from each other. A *leading question* from the teacher evokes comments from students who, through their responses, involve others in the process of learning. *(Grade 1)*

(5) When introducing a new concept, I like to use manipulative aids. First graders seem to grasp a new concept much easier if they can actually touch and explore. I try to have materials available for each student or perhaps for every two students. I like to give the students time to work with the materials--a time for self-exploration. Then I proceed with my lesson by directing the class as to the use of these manipulatives. After adequate time has been given to use of these aids, I use the chalkboard to introduce the written process. I give students turns coming to the board and helping. Then each child is

given a math page that uses this new skill. We do half of the page orally, working through each problem together. Each student completes the second half independently. Upon completion, I check the papers and the students correct any errors. *(Grade 1)*

(7)   I like to use some active participation techniques; that is, I like to have some activities that each student can do at his or her desk and that I can monitor. This will help students see for themselves how the concept develops. I like a form of inquiry approach, but I can't really wait for the concept to develop from random handling of the equipment. I usually guide students through to the final objective with such questions as "What will happen if you do such and such?" I like activities like Action Fractions and Cuisenaire rod developments where I can control the time frame and where the students learn how to use the manipulative to solve the problems of the day. In this way, even if they don't master the stages to the pure symbolic level, they still have a tool that will enable them to solve problems a different way. *(Grade 5)*

(8)   It is important for the child to become involved in *doing* the skill as soon as possible. Just listening is not usually very productive. Since most of my teaching is individualized or in small groups, it is possible to keep the child involved as I present a new skill and to get him or her to try it out quickly. Learn by doing! It is also important to have the child tell what he or she is doing and why. This gets more of the senses involved and hopefully gives the task a *raison d'etre*. *(Grades 3-4)*

(11)   The students' undivided attention is paramount. To curb distraction and enhance concentration, students are asked to remove all books, pencils, etc., from desks and hands. The reason for this action is explained to them in a friendly, concerned manner. I try to stimulate interest and anticipation in learning a new math concept prior to the presentation by using appropriate terms and voice inflections. Building an accepting, anticipatory attitude is important. For emphasis, I write the new sample math problems on the chalkboard larger than I ordinarily would write. *(Grade 3)*

(16)   Generally, when introducing a new concept or skill I try to make it as easy and logical as possible, stressing the basic understanding and assimilation of its parts. This may readily be accomplished through the use of different colored markers and specific example problems with each phase of the concept or skill done in different colors. This process seems to focus the students' attention and establishes a logical sequence of operations for them. The use of illustrations is also beneficial to student understanding. I also try to maintain a continuity of concepts so that no idea arises in a total vacuum. *(Grade 6)*

(17) I try to personalize concepts whenever possible through a physical or hands-on approach. Following are examples of what I do with various concepts of measurement. When teaching perimeter, I have the students march around the classroom. Some students do this a dozen times before they connect the term with its meaning. For the concept of area, students figure the area of our classroom floor and of their bedroom floor at home. They use geoboards for their individual work. For volume, we figure the volume of pails and various other containers as well as discuss the job of a heating engineer or contractor who must determine the size of a radiator or another heating apparatus for a particular classroom. *(Grade 6)*

(20) I vary my presentations and keep them relevant and interesting. I show my students the necessity for math in their lives. We may add prices on shopping receipts, balance checking accounts, figure bowling scores, talk about trips in kilometers using road maps, etc. Vary your approach! *(Grade 4)*

(31) When introducing a computational skill, I have found most children grasp the steps more quickly if I work problems with them using the blackboard or the overhead projector while frequently asking "Now what should we do?" I have also found that the slower children catch on more quickly if allowed to work with a partner in the initial stages. Children love to write on the blackboard and I make use of this. I have enough board space to accommodate half the class at one time. While at the board, the children work out dictated problems. In this way I can quickly identify those who are having difficulty grasping a computational skill. Using manipulative aids is frequently a good way to introduce a concept. Children like to have something to handle. It arouses interest and gets things off to a good start. *(Grade 4)*

(32) To introduce new material I summarize what the students already know and then introduce the new concept by showing how it fits and flows from previous concepts. I use a lecture approach, using the chalkboard and quizzing students as I review previous concepts and introduce new ones. *(Grade 3)*

(42) Motivation is all! I present all concepts at the blackboard. From this position, one glance at the expressions on students' faces determines if they understand, if they are paying attention, etc. I demand (and get) attention. This can be done easily, most often with humor. Early on, the students are told I do not expect them to know all the answers, but they must be able to repeat the question. You only have to enforce this a few times. If you look up and find a sheep straying from the fold, ask a question and then call on that student. The usual comment is, "I didn't hear what you said." My response is, "That's not quite true. What is?" Sheepishly, the student admits, "I wasn't paying attention." My response is, "Ah, now *that's* the truth." No hostility, no nagging, merely go on with the presentation. Whenever possible, I try to use materials not used by previous teachers. For fractions and geometry, I use a publisher's math slides. The novelty of this presentation elicits concentration and I've never had a student who was not eager to participate actively.

I insist that my students take math notes during a presentation. I'm convinced that the act of writing down important concepts assists in learning. On any math worksheet, they are always allowed to refer to their notes--a kind of self-reinforcement occurs. By the time they are tested, they are prepared. For the most part, students decide what notes to take. In the case of a critical rule or concept, I state, "This must be memorized," and write a clear statement on the board to be copied. Irreverence helps. For example, a serious statement on addition of like fractions might end with ". . . and keep your paws off of those denominators!"

Too often children will not ask questions after a presentation because that "labels them as being dumb." I fight this vigorously. After any presentation I ask, "Where's the fog? I know it's out there." With much reassurance that questions reflect their interest in their own education, and so forth, some student will break the ice. That student receives enough praise so that he or she appears to be the star math student of the day.

In a short time students become comfortable with asking questions, viewing it as a sign of intelligence, not stupidity. *(Grades 5-6)*

(44)   In the elementary school classroom I find it helpful if you are dramatic. If you as a teacher are exciting and dramatic, it catches the students' attention as well as motivates them. Second, if at all possible, concepts should be presented in a problem-solving situation. This not only helps develop problem-solving skills, but also helps children see that math is a subject taught to solve real situations and is not just exercises that are ends in themselves. Finally, I also like to play ignorant on how to do a problem. I am quite serious when I do this and then draw from the students the errors of my way. *(Grades 1-5)*

(60)   Generally, I try to introduce a concept by having the students discuss ways in which the "book math" is used in the real world. For instance, they might mention that fractions are used to measure height, age, size, distance, and so on. *(Grades 7-8)*

(62)   First, we discuss the new concept being taught--I show examples on the board, explaining and asking questions as I do this. Second, I explain why we are learning the new idea, how we relate it to our everyday living (if possible), and show how it is a buildup from what we have previously learned. Third, we read our textbook and then the students try to work the examples therein on the board. Fourth, the children do the problems in their workbooks on their own; these are then checked to see if they are having trouble. Finally, I have a reproducible sheet for homework so the concept is reinforced. *(Grade 4)*

(77)   I introduce a concept or skill, whenever possible, by using the concrete, then semi-concrete, followed by the abstract method. *(Grade 3)*

(78)   The teacher's manual has an excellent "Introducing the Lesson" section for each new skill or concept. The introduction may be in the form of manipulative displays, discovery games that lead the students into a new area, or it may be a teacher-directed introduction on the board--learning through examples worked step by step. Again, it depends on what skill is being taught. *(Grade 3)*

(82) I find it helpful to introduce a concept or skill to a small group of children (ten or less). The use of a pretest determines the different levels that children are at, which allows for creating these groups just prior to the introduction of the concept or skill. I also like to touch on various learning styles of the children, whether it be auditory, tactile, or visual. *(Grade 3)*

Exercises for Question 4

1. List the techniques used by the respondents to introduce a concept or skill. Pick three of these techniques that you believe would be particularly effective and explain why you think so.

2. Teachers 16, 32, and 62 make comments which indicate that teaching the structure of mathematics (i.e., the relating of mathematical ideas) is very important to them. Give reasons for teaching the structure of mathematics. Should students be expected to display their understanding of mathematical structure on examinations? Explain.

3. Teachers 5 and 31 mention that they have students work problems at the board. What are the advantages and disadvantages of this technique? How would you manage students' board work? What would you have students who remain in their seats do while others are at the board?

4. Teacher 20 encourages teachers to vary their approach when introducing a new concept. Why is it important to do this? Mention some different approaches that can be used.

5. Teacher 2 mentions the technique of asking questions in teaching a concept or skill. What are the advantages of questioning? What are some pitfalls of questioning?

6. Teacher 8 contrasts learning by listening with learning by doing. What suggestions can you give for helping teachers involve their students more in "doing"? Teacher 42 might suggest that note-taking is part of learning by doing. What is your opinion of this? Explain.

7. **Project.** Read the bulletin "Meaning in Elementary School Mathematics" in *Research Within Reach: Elementary School*

Mathematics (1).   One of the sections in this bulletin, "Maintaining a Meaningful Environment," has suggestions on how teachers might inject discovery and discussion techniques into their teaching. Report on how these suggestions are being implemented by the respondents to Question 4.

8.   **Project.** Many teacher's guides for textbooks offer suggestions for introducing a specific lesson. Select two lessons from a textbook and write a summary of the suggestions for introducing them that are found in the teacher's guide. Are they appropriate? Explain. Do you have better suggestions for introducing each lesson? What are they? (Attach a copy of each lesson.)

Maintaining Skills

Question 5:   What techniques have you found successful in maintaining skills?

Teacher Responses

(3)   I use an occasional five to six minutes at the end of a math period for a puzzle-type question that involves using skills already taught, as well as reproducible worksheets for homework that reinforce previously taught skills. Also, in my efforts to review and reteach a particular skill, I will occasionally call one student to come to the board to be a "mini-teacher" and explain a problem. *(Grades 4-5)*

(4)   I use a lot of games. I drill with flash cards (the students hold up answer cards) and use oral and chalkboard game drills. We have some self-check activities called Turn and Learns and the Digitor, and we work in as much math incidentally during the day as we can (e.g., counting papers, children, books; telling time). *(Grade 1)*

(5)   Every day my students are given a math review sheet. This sheet is completed independently and it is not done during our

regular math period. Any errors made are circled and my students must make corrections and return this work to me. I have review sheets for every new skill taught, and by keeping track of errors I am able to determine the skills for which my students need reinforcement. Perhaps this means total reintroduction of a skill or just additional practice. *(Grade 1)*

(13)   Skills once truly learned usually need only a minimum of maintenance, but a good review schedule is very important. In addition to spiraling lessons in the textbook by going back to preceding pages and by incorporating previous skills into new concepts, including prior skills on later tests also urges students to review again. *(Grades 7-8)*

(26)   Maintaining skills, like anything else, must be done by practice. The important factor is to vary the medium as much as possible. Reproducible worksheets, movies, computers, board work, and special assignments all help to reinforce the skills without boring the students. *(Grade 8)*

(41)   The students have a ten to fifteen minute daily quiz on recently learned skills, which is given at the beginning of the period. There are four columns on the handout. One column is done each day, Monday through Thursday, and is teacher graded each day. *(Grade 7)*

(42)   Nothing beats "drill and practice." I prepare the worksheets for the children and almost always they contain three parts: some review problems of the four basic algorithms (lots of borrowing in subtraction; lots of zeros in multiplication); problems based on concepts previously presented, and finally, problems based on current concepts. Often such "drill and practice" is presented through story problems. *(Grades 5-6)*

(54)   I use a weekly review sheet of sixteen to twenty problems. Each sheet has problems covering the major concepts taught to date. The number of problems per concept is decreased as new concepts are covered and added to the sheet. *(Grade 3)*

Exercises for Question 5

1. List the many different methods used by the respondents for
    maintaining skills. Which one do you find most desirable and
    which one do you find least desirable? Support your choices.
    Do you have a method for maintaining skills that is not one of the
    responses?

2. One method of maintaining skills is to make them part of the
    development of new skills as mentioned by Teacher 13. For
    example, if seventh grade students are finding the average of a set
    of numbers, then have exercises that require them to do this for
    two-digit whole numbers, fractions, and decimals. You can also
    ask them to round off the answer to the nearest hundredth. Give
    the advantages and disadvantages of this maintenance policy as
    compared with that of Teacher 5, who gives out review sheets.

3. Teacher 13 puts previously tested skills on subsequent tests.
    What are your feelings about doing this? Why don't more
    teachers do this?

4. **Project.** Review a grade-level mathematics textbook to find out
    how it promotes the maintenance of skills. Indicate how it is
    done and whether you agree with the textbook's plan. Does this
    textbook force students to review by requiring them to use
    previous skills in working problems that promote the learning of
    new concepts and skills? (See Excercise 2 for examples of this.)
    Explain.

5. **Project.** Read the bulletin "Securing Mathematical Skills: Drill
    and Other Topics" in *Research Within Reach: Elementary School
    Mathematics* (1). Pick three suggestions for maintaining skills
    that were most meaningful to you and explain why you chose
    them.

Developing
Problem-Solving Skills

Question 6: What techniques have you found successful in developing problem-solving skills?

Teacher Responses

(3) A general technique I have found helpful in developing problem-solving skills is to model strategies for the students. For example, I make a drawing of the problem, if possible, and a table of the information that will help in solving it. Sometimes I give problems with extraneous information and have children extract the information that is needed to work the problem. Occasionally I have children close their eyes while we use the "mind's eye" to visualize the problem. Many of my children are poor readers, and I think they may benefit some by this technique. I have many of my poor readers reread the problem once or twice or even three times so that proper labeling may be accomplished. Often we will estimate first, then solve. Also, I will ask, "Does your answer seem reasonable?" I also use commercially prepared problem-solving decks. Since some of my children are poor readers, I use a third grade problem-solving deck along with decks for grades four and five. With these three decks all the children have problem-solving opportunities, with a measure of

success. I also find past issues of the *Arithmetic Teacher* a good resource for problem-solving activities. *(Grades 4-5)*

(4)   I have small groups of children brainstorming a problem; that is, they suggest various ways to attack a problem that may prove to be successful. This is quite popular with my students. *(Grade 1)*

(7)   Sometimes I ask the students to "draw" the problem. Younger children actually draw the cookies and the lines connecting certain numbers of cookies to specific stick figures they have drawn that represent people. Older ones can draw circles for the cookies and x's for the people. I find that trying to draw the action focuses on what has to be done to get the desired results, and seems to lead children to solutions. Children who have difficulty reading problems show greater interest in tape-recorded problems. They have an active interest in solving the problem and are not intimidated by bunches of words.

Calculators have also been fun for problem solving. The children seem to feel they are getting away with something because they don't have to actually figure out the answers. This bypasses computation and helps them to focus on problem solving. When I taught third grade we would have some days when we played Specialist. I would supply the numbers and the result, and they would determine the operation. Then I would work the numbers into a little story and come to the Specialist for his or her diagnosis of which operation was performed. This leads students to figure out their own problems to take to a Specialist, so they learn what kinds of words are common in story problems. *(Grade 5)*

(16)   The use of manipulative aids helps in developing problem-solving skills. The learner can more readily perceive relationships and is encouraged to look for them as he or she is personally involved with manipulating concrete objects and observing the effects. However, whatever techniques you use to teach problem solving, here (as in so many other skills) explanation, practice, and repetition are invaluable. *(Grade 6)*

(17)   I am continually educating the class and individual students on how to analyze and personalize a problem using the following points:

1. Draw a diagram of what is occurring in a problem.
2. Substitute your own name, those of your close friends, and the names of places close to home for any of the names in a problem.
3. Determine what the problem is asking.
4. Solve the problem by using simpler numbers, preferably "easy" whole numbers.
5. Analyze the method or approach you used.
6. Solve the problem again with original values reinstated.
7. Reread the problem and check the sense of your answer.

(Grade 6)

(31) To begin, we simply read problem after problem and decide what operation or combination of operations would be required to solve each one. During this process the children learn to identify key terms that in themselves indicate a specific operation. As we progress to more difficult problems, the children learn to identify relevant and irrelevant information. Given several choices of algorithms to use, children go on to write solutions to the problems. Eventually, the children write their own word problems and show the solutions. To handle word problems well, a child must believe that he or she can do it. *(Grade 4)*

(37) I help students develop their problem-solving skills by asking them questions that demand that they think through problems and by holding all students accountable for trying to apply their knowledge. *(Grade 2)*

(42) I have been working with microcomputers for the past few years. The computer is excellent for promoting problem-solving skills. I have several programs in which they must think math theory in order to play the game, and they love it. Students may work with one or two others; more often, I hook the computer to a large monitor and it becomes a class activity. *(Grades 5-6)*

(44) The CSMP elementary school program makes use of three non-verbal languages that help develop the problem-solving skills of seeing relations, logical thinking, and classification. Arrows are used to show relations among numbers, operations, functions, and ideas. Strings, much like Venn diagrams, allow children to classify and think logically about situations. The Papy minicomputer allows students to do

operations on large numbers even though they're not yet ready to do these operations on paper by themselves. This frees students from being bogged down in computation and allows them to think more about the problem situation. The three languages together free the child, especially the young one or the slow reader, to acquire problem-solving skills without getting bogged down because of his or her deficient reading skills. *(Grades 1-5)*

(52) Vary the mathematical operations needed to solve the problems. For example, rather than doing all story problems that involve addition, mix them up so that many processes have to be used (addition, subtraction, multiplication, and division) to solve the problems. In doing this, students have to think analytically and develop strategies for solving the problems. *(Grades 4-5)*

(55) The CSMP elementary school program taught me a lot about teaching problem-solving skills. The program does not direct students to go right for the answer. They are asked to look at a question in such a way as to be challenged to find answers in more than one way. This is not to discourage students from quick answers but rather to help them become more adept at searching for solutions to a problem. An important step in problem solving is asking the right questions. This leads to discovering strategies and ultimately (it is hoped) to solutions. When children, early in their math experiences, learn to look things over with care and thought, they develop thinking skills. These skills help to promote and nurture problem-solving abilities. The best payoff for all of this is the confidence the children have been gaining about facing problem-solving situations. There is no perfection yet but there's a trend toward improvement. *(Math Lab Teacher, Grades 1-5)*

Exercises for Question 6

1. The National Council of Teachers of Mathematics (NCTM) in its *An Agenda for Action* (2c) recommends that "Problem solving must be the focus of school mathematics in the 80s." To many people the phrase "problem solving" means solving word problems. In the NCTM report this phrase means much more than this. What does the phrase "problem solving" mean to you? To get at a more comprehensive meaning of this phrase, compile a list of the problem-solving skills mentioned by the respondents. What does the NCTM statement quoted above mean to you? Do you agree with it? Explain.

2. Teacher 44 comments that the CSMP elementary school program (3) uses three non-verbal languages to foster problem-solving skills. This teacher concludes that this is particularly helpful for students who lack reading skills. What suggestions do the respondents have for helping students who are deficient in reading skills to become better problem solvers? What suggestions do you have?

3. Teachers 3 and 17 list many problem-solving skills. Teacher 16 implies that problem-solving skills, like any other skill, will not be adequately learned unless they are taught, practiced, and repeated. Do you agree with this teacher? Explain. Is it possible for problem-solving skills to become as commonplace to students as computational skills? Explain.

4. Often students think that there is only one correct way to solve a problem. What difficulties can this misconception cause a student? What can a teacher do to overcome this mindset?

5. Calculators can help students strike a better balance between laboring for computational accuracy and concentrating on problem-solving strategies. Do you agree with this statement? Explain. (A similar statement is made by Teacher 7.)

6. The teaching mode of some teachers can be characterized as a "problem-solving" mode. In this mode, the content is presented by the teacher through leading questions that encourage the students to suggest and discuss different possible responses. Does this appear to be the mode of Teachers 37 and 55? Do you or would you use this mode? Explain.

7. **Project.** Read the bulletin "Mathematical Problem Solving: Not Just a Matter of Words" in *Research Within Reach: Elementary School Mathematics* (1). Write a review of this bulletin as if you were writing for a teachers' journal, your objective being to inform teachers of the bulletin's content and to motivate them to read it.

8. **Project.** Critically review the attention that an elementary or middle school textbook gives to developing problem-solving skills. (Attach sample pages that help support your review.)

Using Manipulative Aids

Question 7: When do you feel it is appropriate to use manipulative aids in your classroom, and how do you manage their use?

Teacher Responses

(5) I use manipulative aids when introducing a new skill. I also let some students continue to use these aids until I feel they are able to visualize the process involved. When manipulatives are first used, the class may seem to play and be disruptive, but they soon learn that a manipulative aid is not a toy but rather a tool. Time needs to be given for exploration, but when that time allotment has been used it is important to instruct the students as to the use of the aid. *(Grade 1)*

(7) I use manipulative aids for many different purposes. We all use them during the introduction of a new concept. As the concept is developed, their use is diminished until only a few students are still using them. As a fifth grade teacher, I find it is better to teach the whole class each new concept and then, during practice time, let the pupils find their own level of attack. Some become immediately impatient with the slowness

of manipulatives and move to the symbolic, while others take a little longer to abandon such help. Others never do move out of this level of thinking during the whole fifth grade year. However, I feel that using aids to do the assignment enables such students to develop the same concepts as their peers, while internalizing relationships on a physical level. *(Grade 5)*

(17) I find that manipulative aids are appropriate when introducing a new concept to a class, group, or individual and during any re-explanation of a concept taught during the year or taught in a previous year that is a difficult one for the average student. When I have insufficient manipulative aids for the entire class, as is the case with metric weights and measures, I demonstrate them to the class as a whole when introducing a concept. The use of aids is encouraged by requiring students to show me proof for a particular answer on a subsequent assignment by using an aid. *(Grade 6)*

(18) I use manipulatives when I feel it will help in understanding the concept being taught. For example, early in the work on perimeters and areas we use geoboards to discuss unit areas, for the development and meaning of area formulas, and for exploring problem-solving techniques used to discover areas of irregular shapes. During work on solid geometry, models of prisms, pyramids, cylinders, cones, etc. are provided. In teaching probability, coins, dice, spinners, etc. are used. Materials are used individually or in small groups depending on the manipulatives involved, the class, and the activity. *(Grades 7-8)*

(24) I feel manipulative and visual aids of a wide variety should be available to students at all times. Manipulatives help students explore new ways to solve problems and gain results by arranging, rearranging, building, and measuring. Experimentation in real-world activities provides for realistic learning. *(Grades 3-5)*

(31) I feel manipulative aids are not only appropriate but also necessary in some units of study, for example, measurement, making change, fractions, and geometry. If there are not enough aids for everyone, or if having everyone doing the same thing would create too much chaos, I have the children operate in small groups with an indicated leader, if necessary.

At times manipulative aids may be needed only for demonstration or for use with a small number of children who are having difficulty grasping a concept. *(Grade 4)*

(40) I use manipulative aids when presenting some lessons. A demonstration clock is used when teaching time, and then students are each given smaller clocks to use with group instruction. Magnetic money is used on the chalkboard so that the whole class can develop an understanding before counting real change. Attribute blocks are used to develop logic. Tangrams, triangles, and squares are used in geometry lessons. The demonstration Papy minicomputers actively involve the children in the lesson, and then they have the opportunity to work further with their own desk minicomputers. I feel it is essential to have enough manipulative aids for each child so that a whole directed lesson can be developed using them. When each child has the same item, it is easier to teach the use of it and encourage creative exploration with it. *(Grade 2)*

(52) Manipulative aids are used in my classroom to introduce a concept, to help children who have difficulties understanding a concept, and to enrich an idea. I use them with the total group, with small groups, with individuals, in a lab situation where an aide is present, and for rainy day activities. Management becomes easy if the rules are established from the very beginning. The rules include who will be responsible for returning a game or activity to a designated area and the proper use of the materials while being used. *(Grades 4-5)*

(55) I use manipulatives more frequently in the lower grades, but I use them when the circumstances warrant their use, no matter what the grade. As time goes on many students move away from using these things. However, it has been my experience that children have different rates for doing this. This is a very individual matter. I never push a child to make a break if he or she is not ready. Sometimes a child is ready to leave some of the early manipulatives but will need some encouragement to do so. Tender loving care is in order here! *(Math Lab Teacher, Grades 1-5)*

Exercises for Question 7

1. List how the respondents use manipulative aids. Do you agree with each use? If not, why not? Can you add to this list?

2. Teacher 17 requires her students to justify a result by using a manipulative aid. That is, not only is this teacher using aids to assist her students in their learning, but she is also demanding that they demonstrate their ability to use them. Would you demand this? Explain.

3. Teacher 17, a middle school teacher, mentions the use of manipulative aids as a remedial tool. What are your thoughts on the appropriateness of using manipulative aids for remediation at upper grade levels? What advice can you give for how to use manipulatives with upper grade-level students?

4. One role of a teacher is to integrate the use of manipulatives into an instructional unit. What does this mean? Why is it important to do this?

5. The following quotation is taken from page 22 of *Research Within Reach: Elementary School Mathematics* (1): "Of the K-6 teachers surveyed, nearly half reported that their students use manipulatives less than once a week, or not at all. There is compelling evidence from research for incorporating regular work with manipulatives into every classroom and with every child--from the elementary level on into the secondary level." What are some hindrances to the use of manipulative aids by teachers? How can each of these hindrances be overcome?

6. **Project.** Critique the bulletin "The Role of Manipulatives in Elementary School Mathematics" in *Research Within Reach: Elementary School Mathematics* (1).

7. **Project.** Write a lesson plan in which students, as part of the plan, use a manipulative aid to learn a mathematical concept such as fractions, adding with carrying, place value, or perimeter.

Using the Textbook

Question 8:   How do you use the textbook?

In responding to this question, mention such things as (1) variation in number of pages covered per day, (2) the types of reading and problem assignments made, and (3) when the text is used.

Teacher Responses

(3)   My students work in the text at their own pace. Some children are on page 170 while the less able are on page 112. Some will do two complete lessons in a day while the less able will take almost two days to complete one lesson. But I am firm and demand attentiveness to the business at hand! Most students are well motivated and work to their capacity. I never hold a child back for my convenience. If a student can handle the next lesson, or next unit, he or she is welcome to move ahead under my watchful eye, knowing that I am always available if help is needed. Nothing pleases me more than to see a student move ahead and achieve some independence and accept some responsibility for his or her learning.

Another way I use the text is for development of mental arithmetic. For example, if a student knows his or her basic multiplication and division facts, I allow him or her to come to me and do the next lesson orally. For example, from knowing the basic fact 6 x 4 = 24, I allow the student to do these expanded problems orally from the textbook:

$$\begin{array}{ccc} 40 & 400 & 4000 \\ \underline{\times\ 6} & \underline{\times\ 6} & \underline{\times\ 6} \end{array}$$

I believe that having oral arithmetic skills is important. *(Grades 4-5)*

(6)   I sometimes use the explanation offered in the text for a new concept if I feel the explanation is a good one. The students and I read the explanation together. If I feel the text explanation is poor, then the text is used only for practice problems. The number of pages covered daily depends on the number of problems on a page and how much time is required for their completion. We use a supplemental text when more practice problems are required. *(Grade 5)*

(7)   When we developed our mathematics continuum, we recommended that the school board adopt three textbooks so teachers could choose from a range of sources. I use two of these textbooks and three sets of reproducible masters. I decide on the objective for the week, teach it through active participation, and select from all the sources available which pages, materials, and activities will best teach to the objective. The more difficult the concept, the more material I might use. I also use a "homework text." This is a discontinued series that I pass out to the students at the beginning of the year. They keep these books at home for assignments to be done there. I select appropriate activities from the index of this book to supplement our classroom work and assign them as homework. *(Grade 5)*

(16)   The textbook is used daily by all students with the length of assignment based on student ability. The average group is expected to complete two pages a day while the advanced group is to complete four pages per day or twenty pages per week broken up as they choose. Students are encouraged to read the author's development of a concept on their own, with the intent being that practice and experience will aid the student in careful and accurate reading. In most instances, mistakes made by misinterpreting what the authors say are in themselves a learning experience, and when identified, enhance the learner's confidence and ability to more accurately interpret directions. When assistance is needed, it is provided in a manner that encourages the learner to discover the error and subsequently recognize it in the future. *(Grade 6)*

(22)   Directions in the book are always read orally by a student or myself. Given assignments are always written on the board to avoid the "Oh! I didn't know . . ." or "Didn't you say . . ." syndrome. Problems are not assigned by the entire page if they number more than fifteen. Only the odd or the even numbers are assigned if a page has more than fifteen problems. The problems left over from the page may then be assigned to a special help group as an in-class assignment, homework, or as board work. *(Grade 6)*

(43)   Our basic course material comes from the text that is used to teach students to read and understand mathematics. I cover anywhere from one to five pages in a lesson and combine sections of the book that are related or contrast two concepts. The main source of assignments is the text, with students having some type of assignment every day except the day of a test. *(Grade 8)*

(50)   I plan for one chapter at a time. I prepare support and enrichment material to correlate with the concepts in the chapter. If appropriate, I pretest, especially if the chapter is mostly computation. I never assign all the problems on a page. I'm of the view that if a student can do five to ten problems well, any more is redundant. I use the ideas presented on the teacher's page. *(Grades 4-5)*

(65)   I use the textbook for problem assignments. I rarely use it for the students' initial exposure to a concept. I cover one or two pages daily depending upon the difficulty of the concept and the needs of my students. Occasionally I skip pages that are too easy, difficult, or confusing for my students. I also skip, and later return to, material that is inappropriately placed or that blends better with our other subjects at a later time. I am selective regarding assignments; I do not automatically assign the whole page. *(Grade 6)*

Exercises for Question 8

1. Teacher 6 makes the comment that "The students and I read the explanation together." What are the advantages and disadvantages of doing this? How frequently would you do this, and how much does your answer depend on the grade level?

2. Teachers 22 and 50 comment on the number of textbook problems that they assign. Give and support your policy in this regard.

3. Suppose you have a textbook that contains answers to the odd-numbered problems but not to the even-numbered ones. Why would you want to assign some odd-numbered problems? Even-numbered problems? In general, what percent of the problems you assign would be odd numbered?

4. Teachers 3, 6, 16, 43, and 65 indicate either implicitly or explicitly that they use or do not use the textbook's explanation to introduce a concept. When would you *not* use the textbook's explanation? Would you have your students read the explanation in the textbook if you didn't use it? Explain.

5. **Project.** Read the bulletin "The Teacher and the Textbook" from *Research Within Reach: Elementary School Mathematics* (1). What does research say about the shortcomings of textbooks? What responsibility does this place on the teacher?

6. **Project.** Select two textbooks from different publishers for a specific grade. Find a topic in which the textbooks differ significantly in their problem sets for that topic. In what ways do they differ? Which of the two problem sets do you prefer? Explain. What would you do if your textbook had an undesirable problem set? (Attach copies of the problem sets to your comments.)

Using Workbooks

Question 9: How do you use the workbook?

In responding to this question, mention such things as (1) variation in number of pages covered per day, (2) the types of problem assignments made, and (3) when workbooks are used.

Teacher Responses

(17) Possibly as many as one to three students in any given year may be given a workbook. These are the students whose organizational and work-study skills are so weak that an assignment on loose-leaf paper is seldom completed or turned in. It is hoped that the workbook can be more easily monitored by the teacher, parent, and student. Rarely have I found workbooks effective for more than three to four weeks. Those students usually discover it is much more interesting and rewarding to work with the rest of the class than on page after page in a pictureless workbook. *(Grade 6)*

(21) The workbook is used in the morning for independent seatwork. The page covered is usually a review of what was completed the afternoon before. *(Grade 2)*

(24) We have no workbook to accompany the text. However, I have several workbooks from various publishers that students use as resources. Sheets are often pulled from the workbooks for certain individuals who need additional work. *(Grades 3-5)*

(25) I do not use a workbook. Our district does not purchase the supplemental workbook for math. I feel that the text and reproducible sheets are sufficient. *(Grade 3)*

(45) I've always managed to get a copy of an accompanying workbook, although workbooks have never been affordable to my school system. Individual pages are reproduced and usually given as homework, or I may use parts of pages as quizzes or tests.   *(Grades 3-4)*

Exercises for Question 9

1. List the uses that the respondents have for a workbook. Can you add to this list?

2. Teacher 17 uses a workbook to help students who have poor organizational and work-study skills. She mentions that this use of a workbook is not effective for a long period of time. Do you think this is a good use of a workbook? Explain. How would you handle these students' problems?

3. **Project.** Analyze a workbook that accompanies a particular textbook. What reasons and suggestions are given by the authors for using the workbook? Compare the types of problems that are in the workbook with those that are in the textbook. In what way would you use this workbook and with what students? Would you recommend that your school buy this workbook to supplement the textbook? Why?

Using Reproducible Materials

Question 10:   How do you use reproducible materials?
In responding to this question, mention such things as (1) number of pages per day and (2) when they are used.

Teacher Responses

(5)   I use reproducible pages mainly for review and practice. I usually give one page each morning as a seatwork activity. After these pages are checked, students must correct all errors and return the work to me. I use this as a diagnostic tool. If many children have difficulty, I know the skill needs more explanation and practice. *(Grade 1)*

(14)   I rely on reproducible sheets from *Mathimagination* for skills practice and assignments for particular groups. I use our textbook's enrichment masters as content for better students, and *Aftermath* pages for the whole class for variety. I try to provide an assignment each day for one of my three groups while working with the other two. Frequently, these assignments are from reproducible materials. *(Grade 5)*

(24) I prefer making my own spirit masters to using commercial ones, as they are more personal (my students' names are in the problems), more timely (the problems depict events occurring in the school, community, etc.), and better cover what the individual is studying. *(Grades 3-5)*

(25) The children are given a "seatwork" packet in the morning to complete while I teach reading in a small group setting. Usually, two of these papers are reproducible pages pertaining to math. They are sheets that correlate with the text. One sheet usually is on the specific skill we are learning that particular week, but I make sure we have previously introduced the skill in our afternoon time set aside for math. The other sheet is generally on a math topic we have covered and mastered some time previously in the school year. This sheet is designed to reinforce a skill already mastered. *(Grade 3)*

(32) I use reproducible sheets to reinforce skills that students have not yet attained after textbook work. For lower ability students I may use reproducible pages instead of textbook work. This allows students to do more work since they are not being hindered by having to copy problems. *(Grade 3)*

(34) I use reproducible pages as supplemental material. They have a variety of formats that make math more enjoyable to learn. The pages I use contain crossword puzzles, bingo games, mystery stories, etc., all of which motivate my students. I also use reproducible materials to help give additional practice to my students when I feel the textbook does not have enough work pages on a particular concept. Generally, the reproducible sheets involve only a small amount of reading and have anywhere from twelve to twenty problems on them. There might be from one to five reproducible pages on math skills handed out in a week. *(Grade 4)*

(36) I use reproducible materials for drill, to cover topics not included in the CSMP elementary school program, in an interest center, and when I have a substitute teacher. *(Grade 3)*

(42) I make up my spirit masters. The actual problems I use are determined by performance on previous worksheets. Students average two or three worksheets a week. The worksheets are also used to increase motivation. Given a paper with only a

few errors, I may say to a student, "Clean up these errors in two seconds and I'll give you one hundred percent." Though I note the kind of errors that have been made, the worksheet is marked 100%. This produces a very positive reaction. Students eagerly make their corrections. This snowballs so that they begin to try for a genuine one hundred percent on the first try. I feel it is critical that math papers be returned to the students as quickly as possible. I usually do it immediately, that is, during the actual work period. As a result, the drudgery of routine computation is eliminated; students treat the experience almost as a game that must be won.

I also use the worksheets to teach test-taking skills, e.g., management of stress and time. Although basic computation is always involved, I take care that the pages do not always look alike; e.g., addition problems may be aligned vertically one time and horizontally the next time. Often I prepare worksheets providing multiple choice answers, along with an answer sheet where students have to darken a circle, as in standardized tests. *(Grades 5-6)*

Exercises for Question 10

1. What are some uses for reproducible materials given by the respondents? Can you add some of your own?

2. What advantages and disadvantages do you see in using commercial reproducibles masters in comparison to teacher-constructed reproducibles? (See comments by Teachers 14, 24, 34, and 42.)

3. Do you have any problem with Teacher 32's reason for using reproducible sheets with lower ability students? Explain.

4. Give reasons why teachers at a particular grade level may want to jointly plan for the construction or selection of appropriate reproducible materials.

5. **Project.** Write a critique of the reproducible worksheets for a specific grade level that accompany a textbook series. Include the authors' objectives and the suggestions given for the use of these

reproducibles. Also, describe the type of content generally included in the reproducible sheets; i.e., is the content computational, enrichment, developmental? (Attach sample copies of these reproducible sheets.)

6. **Project.** There are a number of non-textbook commercial publishers of reproducible materials. These materials can be found in such places as teacher stores and publishers' catalogs. Obtain different types of these reproducibles that you like and write a review of them that includes suggestions on how to use them in the classroom. Write the review as if it will be given to other teachers. (Attach the reproducible sheets to your review.)

Working a Lesson
Without Teacher Explanation

Question 11: How frequently do you allow your students to work through a lesson by their own reading without your explanation? What are your feelings on this?

Teacher Responses

(7) I don't do this and I don't believe in it. Even if it is a refresher lesson, I want to do some teaching, elicit some responses, begin a mindset, and plant a concept a little more firmly. *(Grade 5)*

(17) Most of the explanations in our textbook are done well and are usually not too difficult for an above average reader and math student. I am extremely pleased when a student in my classroom has the ability and the motivation to read the explanations and do the work on his or her own and is able to realize when help is needed. Even the attempt to do so pleases me, for it means the student is interested enough in math to try it alone. That is what the high achievers do regularly, perhaps with some occasional nudging, and what the upper average do somewhat less consistently. The more average math students (in ability or motivation) usually need a specific assignment

with the explanation, and so forth, that precedes it. I realize that a student at this level may miss a basic point if he or she tries a page alone, but I never discourage it. Those missed spots are caught and retaught after a review quiz. *(Grade 6)*

(19) Almost never. This is probably one of my shortcomings. I spoon-feed my students too much. They come to rely on me to explain even the simplest problems before they try to solve them. *(Grades 7-8)*

(23) Unless it's an entirely new concept, I frequently have students read the lesson and proceed without my help. Sometimes in doing this they will make a lot of mistakes, but they will remember all those corrections they had to do and gain more from this type of experience. I feel they also gain a sense of responsibility in doing something on their own, which can be very positive for many students. *(Grade 2)*

(24) This is the main way my math program is structured. It has proven (in existence for fourteen years) to be very effective in that it promotes a sense of student responsibility and commitment; emphasizes the importance of reading and following directions; instills a feeling of pride in the ability to accomplish a task; and allows each student to progress at his or her own pace, with guidance. The student understands that immediate assistance is available for any individual learning need. At the conclusion of each math session, students articulate their learning experiences, emphasizing what each accomplished, how they distributed their time, their feelings about what they have learned, and a schedule of work for the following day, with the teacher doing the same. If they are in a group situation, other learners often offer assistance to those who ask for extra help. *(Grades 3-5)*

(31) How frequently I allow students to work through a lesson on their own depends on the ability of the students. Those in the top group may do so several times a week; they may also work together. I have found that often these children prefer to attempt the work on their own and seek my help only when they cannot collectively arrive at the solution. Children of average ability may occasionally be asked to work through a new lesson. More often they are asked to go on with a particular previously taught skill without benefit of review first. I rarely ask the slower children to try something new on their own. I have found that most of these children will not even attempt to do the lesson. Frequently, they have developed "I can't" attitudes about themselves. I feel I must at least get them rolling in the right direction before I leave them on their own. *(Grade 4)*

(32)   How often I do this depends on the students' ability. Teachers can overteach by doing too much for students. They undermine the development of the students' reasoning ability. *(Grade 3)*

(52)   I think there is much to be gained from a group discussion and my demonstration. Much more can come out of a lesson because of it, and it opens up new avenues of thinking about problems and strategies that may be used in solving them. However, I feel there *must be a balance* between allowing the children to think critically about a problem and giving them too much information. *(Grades 4-5)*

(58)   In first grade there is very little reading. Directions are simple and mainly visual. I tell students to think about how to do a set of problems and then listen to my directions to see if they are right. *(Grade 1)*

(61)   It is a necessary part of teaching. How can children learn from their readings in future years, mathematics or otherwise, if they are not taught to do so now? A teacher will not always be available or be willing to explain the material. *(Grade 5)*

(64)   For a new concept, I'll explain and give examples. To work problems involving a repeated concept, students must read the directions and prior pages that previously dealt with the concept. *(Grades 5-6)*

(66)   I always look over the lesson to see if the children can handle the material on their own. If so, I require them to read it. In this way they are developing independence, will have better retention, and are challenging themselves. They feel a greater achievement, especially if the teacher gives a lot of praise. *(Grade 4)*

(73)   The enrichment activities I give my students are always read by them before I get involved. They read their own textbook instructions probably once or twice per unit . I view this as a

weaning process. It should be handled in such a way that they do not become overly frustrated. *(Grade 3)*

(79)   I do this about four or five times a month. I think it's good for students. They find out how well they can read the material and understand directions, and they are usually better listeners when I explain. *(Grade 8)*

Exercises for Question 11

1. List the reasons given by the respondents for having students read a lesson on their own. If you do not agree with a particular reason, explain why. Can you add to this list? List the respondents' reasons for not having students read a lesson on their own. If you do not agree with a particular reason, explain why. Can you add to this list? Give your response to Question 11.

2. List all the conditions you can find under which the respondents would have their students read a lesson without teacher explanation first. Which ones do you disagree with? Why? Can you add some conditions to this list?

3. How would you counter these remarks made by a seventh and eighth grade teacher in response to Question 11: "I never do. Through the years I find that trying to read the textbook only confuses the students. I sometimes 'translate' the homework directions only to have students reply, 'Why didn't they say that's what they wanted!' I feel it's my job to teach and decode for them."

4. What are some techniques you would use to help students develop their ability to read a lesson on their own?

5. A strong tendency for students working on their own would be to look for the rule associated with a concept and then manipulate the numbers according to the rule without understanding the concept. What advice can you give to help students overcome this tendency?

6. Teacher 17 encourages students to read on their own even knowing that they will make mistakes. Why is it beneficial to the student to be allowed to make mistakes?

7. Teacher 79 mentions that her students listen better if they read the material before she explains it. Give reasons why this might be the case. How can a teacher get students to read material in the textbook before the next day's lesson?

8. **Project.** Write a critical review of a grade-level mathematics textbook using the criterion of how well it is written for students to work through a lesson by their own reading without teacher explanation. Is there much variation in this regard from one lesson to another? Is the book written primarily for the teacher to teach from or for the student to learn from? Is this the way it should be? (Attach sample pages that help support your review.)

9. **Project.** Select a specific lesson from a grade-level mathematics textbook that seems to do a good job of presenting a new concept. Suppose you intend to have your students read this alone, prior to any specific explanation by you. What general and specific comments will you make beforehand that will help students approach this reading, including comments on motivating the concept, an overview of the reading, what you expect of them, and what your role will be? (Attach a copy of the lesson to your comments.)

Keeping and Using Mathematical Records

Question 12:   What types of mathematical records do you keep for each student, and how do you use them?

Teacher Responses

(3)   I keep records of all tests by recording letter grades in the grade book. Occasional brief quizzes are also recorded. With the individualized program I have, I collect papers at the end of each math period. I try very hard to grade them that night and return them the next day with personal notes. If the paper says "See me, please" or "Correct and return," the student knows I have not recorded that he or she has done that lesson. The student must then do the corrections or see me about his or her work before I consider the lesson complete. Sometimes I allow children to grade themselves so they get immediate feedback. I then collect this homework and simply record that homework was done.

Each quarter I use a column in the grade book for recording in pencil the page number that each child is doing. When the lesson is completed satisfactorily, I can easily change the penciled page number in the grade book. I keep it current and can tell at a glance what lesson each student is on for any given day. It is this method that permits me to grant freedom to students to move ahead at their own pace. *(Grades 4-5)*

(4)   I keep checklists for each module. I record the date that each student completed the module. I add a few comments in an abbreviated form that will give an idea of how the child did. For example, *tr* means had trouble, *occ err* means occasional errors, *rev* means reverses numbers and *1-1* means needs much one-to-one help. A quick glance at the sheet gives me a general idea of where the class is as a whole, or where an individual child is. I make anecdotal notations on a particular problem a child is having. If I see that several children are having the same problem, then there is a need to group them together for more instruction and reinforcement.

Our school district has a math record that follows the child from first grade through twelfth grade. At the end of the year we record modules presented, modules mastered, specific strengths and weaknesses, and anything else that might be helpful to succeeding teachers. As a first grade teacher I must begin the record. I try to give information that will assist the second grade teacher and also accurately state the child's beginning understandings in math. *(Grade 1)*

(7)   We keep a wall chart listing each child's name, and along the bottom, each separate skill he or she is to master. When the skill is mastered, the child gets a bright colored spot to place on the chart. The child monitors his or her own progress and comes to the teacher when he or she feels ready to master a previously failed skill. A chart displaying similar skills is in the child's regular file, and a photocopy is included with each report card. This way parents can see the skills for the grade, those taught but not mastered, and those taught and mastered. I also keep a regular grade book with letter grades for the practice work done from the text and spirit masters in class, as well as a record of the homework assignments. In this book I also note particular areas of difficulty to discuss with the child, parent, or the child's tutor. *(Grade 5)*

(16)   Student records consist of daily scores on assignments and weekly test scores. Assignment scores are kept mainly as a vehicle for seeing that assignments are done. Further, each student is expected to redo all problems missed on an assignment with a score of less than seventy-five percent. The weekly test scores are used as an assessment of progress and mastery, with an eighty-five percent average as a minimum standard. *(Grade 6)*

(22) My personal record book indicates every skill mastered. Records help me turn weaknesses into strengths. The name of the game is eighty percent or above equals mastery. Records also help me determine grades, and suggest proper math placement at the junior high level. *(Grade 6)*

(28) I check students' notebooks once every two weeks. What I want to see for each day are their notes on the material I have presented, the homework assigned and completed, followed by corrections for all of the incorrect problems. If these items are in order, the student receives a +4. Each missing assignment gets a -2. Insufficient work gets a -1. The lowest score is a -10. Failure to turn in a notebook earns a -10. The notebook grades are averaged and added on to the student's test and quiz average. The most a score can increase is +4 and the lowest it can fall is -10. It pays to do homework in my class. *(Grades 7-8)*

(34) A student's math record includes the Stanford and the State of Michigan Assessment test scores; timed addition, subtraction, multiplication, and division facts test scores (seven minutes per 100 problems); and pretest and posttest scores in math skills. These test scores help to determine math grouping throughout the school year and indicate what skills need to be concentrated on at school and at home. *(Grade 4)*

(39) Daily grades are kept on students' assignments; they count 1/6 of the report card grade. Quiz grades are averaged once a week and count 2/6 of the report card grade. Chapter tests count 3/6 of the report card grade. *(Grade 7)*

(40) I keep examples of the children's work and a grade book with scores that indicate their proficiency in each skill. These help me later when writing reports. *(Grade 2)*

Exercises for Question 12

1. List the types of records used by the respondents. What types of records do you or will you keep?

2. List the uses that the respondents have for their records. What uses do you or will you make of your records?

3. Give the advantages and disadvantages of the following record-keeping technique used by Teacher 7: Using a wall chart for recording the skills mastered or not yet mastered by a student.

4. Teachers 3 and 28 have their students correct any problems that they missed on an assignment. How important is it to have students do this? Why would a teacher *not* do this?

5. Discuss the advantages and disadvantages of the relative weights that Teacher 39 assigns to daily work, quiz grades, and chapter tests for arriving at a report card grade. What weights would you assign?

Evaluating a Student's Math Knowledge

Question 13: How do you determine throughout the year which mathematical concepts and skills each student has attained?

Teacher Responses

(4) Our math series has written module tests that I often use. However, I prefer oral questioning and activities requiring application of manipulative objects. I like to personally play games with the children so I can observe their strategies, their computations, etc. *(Grade 1)*

(10) I use the school district's math objectives. There is a short test for each objective. The test usually consists of four problems per objective. If a child is successful in three out of four problems, he or she passes the objective. *(Grades 3-4)*

(18) Through their work on frequent quizzes and tests, oral discussion during class, class assignments, homework, standardized tests, and a year-end objective test. *(Grades 7-8)*

(35)   In our math textbook series, each chapter has a pretest and posttest and a "Sharpening Skills" section (which reviews previous chapters), in addition to a "Chapter Check-Up" that is a review of concepts that should have been mastered. These, together with ten of my problems per week, reveal my students' skills. *(Grade 6)*

(55)   In several ways every math program has a predetermined set of concepts and skills to be taught for each grade. One way to see if they are accomplished is by written tests. Such tests are given to fifth graders weekly, sometimes to fourth graders, and rarely to younger groups. Classroom participation is an important way for me to see how the children are doing; noticing how children think is very illuminating. Observing students in written and oral work tells me a lot about their understanding. If they can apply something they already know to a new situation, then I know things are going well for them. There are surely more ways than this for knowing where a child is at regarding his or her work, but I believe I've presented the general idea. Keeping in touch with the child in every way possible is the summation. *(Math Lab Teacher, Grades 1-5)*

Exercises for Question 13

1.   List the ways in which the respondents attain the objective of this question. How would you answer the question?

2.   Teacher 4 uses oral questioning, manipulative activities, and games to observe the childrens' strategies and computations. Are these effective ways to determine a child's understanding of a concept or skill? Explain. Are they good techniques to use at all grade levels? Explain. Can they be substituted for written tests? Explain.

3.   Many teachers and textbook publishers construct tests that are very narrow in the range of cognitive skills that are covered. These tests often stress lower level cognitive skills such as computation, and forsake higher level cognitive skills like the understanding of concepts and problem solving. Is a steady diet of this type of examination harmful to students? Explain.

4. Teacher 18 mentions the use of standardized mathematics tests. What information is gained from administering standardized mathematics tests that is not gained from other forms of testing? Is it important to give them? Explain. How can standardized mathematics tests be misused?

5. Teacher 10 tests all the math objectives on a list of objectives that define her math program. She should then know which concepts and skills each of her students have attained. Many teachers do not test from such a list. How will they know which objectives each of their students have attained? Is this important to know? Explain.

6. **Project.** For a particular grade-level mathematics textbook, select two chapter posttests. Read the chapter that is associated with each test. Then determine the number of problems on each test that test computational skills, test an understanding of concepts, test applications, and test more advanced problem-solving skills (like problems for "experts"). For each test, indicate which problems you would delete and what problems you would add. Overall, do the tests cover a wide range of cognitive objectives? Should they? (Attach copies of each test.)

7. **Project.** Read the bulletin "Diagnosis: Taking the Mathematical Pulse" in *Research Within Reach: Elementary School Mathematics* (1) and write a summary of its content. Do you agree with its conclusion? Explain.

Sources for Written Tests

Question 14:   What are your sources for written tests?

Teacher Responses

(25) I use the textbook's posttests to evaluate overall knowledge on each chapter. They are well organized, easy to score, and are designed to pinpoint areas of weakness at a glance. *(Grade 3)*

(28) I use a combination of other teachers' ideas, textbook publishers' tests (which I find too easy), tests jointly written by myself and a fellow teacher, problems from chapter assignments, and resource books I've collected from serving on book selection committees. *(Grades 7-8)*

(29) Our textbook has excellent chapter review pages and tests. *(Grade 6)*

(52) My school district has a series of fifteen assessment booklets that are administered periodically. The topics cover all operations in whole numbers and fractions, measurement, and pre-algebra. The items included in the booklets were written to assess my school's math objectives and the state's minimum

math objectives. In addition, I write my own tests from time to time and also use tests provided by the textbook publisher. *(Grades 4-5)*

(55) Fifth grade tests usually come from one of two sources. One source is the CDA workbook, where there is an evaluation page after several pages of problems. I reproduce this page and give it as a weekly test. Some children notice that the test is a page from their book and some do not. It is no secret. My mission is to see if children are comprehending, not to be tricky. My other source for tests is me. If I think the evaluation page is not particularly indicative of what the children have done for the week, I make one that is more on target. The fourth grade tests are usually teacher-made. Tests are used to evaluate. How are the children doing? What's going badly? What's going well? What needs work? Who needs help? My aim is to have the tests work *for* the children, not against them. In the lower grades the workbooks and worksheets serve this purpose. *(Math Lab Teacher, Grades 1-5)*

(63) With the exception of the Stanford Diagnostic Math Test and the Iowa Test of Basic Skills, which are given district wide, my math tests are teacher-made. I do not use the tests provided by the textbook publisher since I want my tests to emphasize those areas that I stress in my instruction. Also, by making my own tests I can use vocabulary in the test directions that is suitable for the group being tested. I want a math test, not a reading test! *(Grade 6)*

Exercises for Question 14

1. List the sources for written tests given by the respondents. Can you add to this list?

2. Two of the major sources of written tests are textbook publishers and teachers. What are the advantages and disadvantages of each type of test? Which type do you prefer and why?

3. What advantages are there to having teachers discuss each other's tests? How might this be promoted?

4. **Project.** Read the article "Teacher-Made Tests: Development and Use" by William Mckillip in the November 1979 issue of the *Arithmetic Teacher*. Write a summary of the article. What impact does it have on your perspective on testing?

Assignments

Question 15a: How frequently do you give assignments to be completed in class? How is each assignment scored? What use is made of the score?

Teacher Responses

(13) About half of the assignments given are to be completed in class. My purpose is to train the student in meeting his or her responsibility to finish class assignments. I personally do not grade the daily assignments, but let the students grade their own work. When they grade their assignment, I solicit the answers from the class in a round robin manner. I collect the papers and record the scores, which are used with the test average for a report card grade. *(Grades 7-8)*

(14) The only time I give an assignment that must be completed in class would be an assignment of three or four problems that I give immediately at the end of a skill-oriented lesson. Each student must have it checked and rework incorrect problems. No further use is made of the score. *(Grade 5)*

(25) Students have daily in-class assignments in math. I try to judge the number of problems the majority can complete in the time allotted. Students do not always finish all the work in the time allotted and are instructed to take it home, finish it, and return it the next day. I count the number wrong on each paper and place the score in my grade book. The scores are averaged to determine an assignment grade for each student's report card. *(Grade 3)*

(34) An in-class assignment is given every day. If it is not completed in class that day, it is done as homework. Most students can complete the assignment in class. Often, slower students will have to take it home. The assignment is checked and used by me as an indicator of whether a student is understanding the concept presented. If the student does not understand, then extra individual or small group help is given. *(Grade 4)*

(45) During the course of a week I might give two in-class assignments. However, I prefer to use class time for teacher-student interaction, i.e., question and answer periods, demonstrations, and "You explain to me how I would . . . " activities. The assignments are checked for accuracy and understanding, but no number score is given (only "good," "fair," or "see me!"). *(Grades 3-4)*

(47) I introduce a lesson and then give an assignment appropriate to the time remaining in the class period. Ninety-five percent of the students finish in this time period or by the end of the day. I would say that maybe two or three students take this work home. I use a regular grading scale: 90-100 (A), 80-90 (B), etc. I will make comments on a paper if a concept is misunderstood. If it is totally misunderstood, I will go over it with the child and assign him or her ten other problems to do. *(Grade 3)*

(52) Assignments are given daily to be completed in class. Key assignments are collected and I grade them. Some assignments are checked by the students in class and sometimes they are checked by an adult helper. I use the scores as an indicator for reteaching or moving forward, and also as one of many ways to determine, for the report card, whether specific objectives are mastered. *(Grades 4-5)*

(55) In the CSMP elementary school program, the lessons are teacher guided every step of the way. Most lessons in first, second, and third grade are written like a script. There are no in-class assignments other than the workbooks and worksheets. These materials are frequently used by the students and are not typical of materials with these names. In the fourth grade CSMP program, the children are also guided closely by the teacher, but a little less so than in the earlier grades. Because the nature of this program is so teacher directed, there is not much time left for traditional class assignments. *(Math Lab Teacher, Grades 1-5)*

Exercises for Question 15a

1. Give advantages and disadvantages of each scoring plan: students score their own assignments; students score their classmates' assignments; teachers score the assignments. How frequently should a teacher score the assignments? Explain.

2. Make a list of the uses that the respondents have for a student's score on an in-class assignment. How would you use this score?

3. Give reasons for having students start assignments in class. Under what conditions would you have them start an assignment outside of class?

4. Give reasons for having students finish assignments in class. (See Teachers 13 and 14 for some suggestions.) How often would you follow this practice? Explain.

Question 15b: How frequently do you give assignments to be completed outside of class? How is each assignment scored? What use is made of the score?

Teacher Responses

(2)   Homework is assigned several times a week. I grade the homework and record the scores. First grade children usually like homework and I strive to make it a fun learning activity. *(Grade 1)*

(4)   Occasionally I will assign an information-gathering task that includes such things as looking at home for shapes, objects with numerals on them, and sets having a specific number of objects. I also have children listen at home for how many times numbers are mentioned. The information is shared and made into lists, graphs, posters, etc. I mentally make note of children who do not participate. Rather than assigning homework for first graders, I prefer that their parents play math games with them. However, if a child is a rather pokey worker but understands the concepts, then I send work home to be completed and returned to me. I also send assignments home if a child is absent for four or more days. *(Grade 1)*

(11)   Homework is assigned only to students who have been absent and have missed certain class assignments. There is one exception to the "homework only for absentees" policy. That is, from the day that the multiplication tables are introduced, each student is asked to write the tables they are working on twice each evening at home. They are not required to turn the paper in. I solicit (during early parent conferences) the help of parents in seeing to it that this assignment is done each evening. *(Grade 3)*

(26)   Every assignment I give, in or out of class, is to be done in the student's notebook. We then check the assignment collectively. No grade is given for the assignment except for the notation "complete" or "not complete." Students are told that homework or classwork is the place to make mistakes. No one is penalized for an assignment that is all wrong as long as the student has tried. After checking their work, students must redo all problems that were incorrectly done before the notebook is checked and graded at the end of the chapter. The grades that are received for the notebook at the end of each chapter are assigned point values of +2 (A), +1 (B), 0 (C), -1 (D), -2 (E), and -5 (not turned in). These points are then added to the student's final grade average. *(Grade 8)*

(33)   Since students work at different paces, an assignment given one day is always due the following day. The assignment is always started in class. This way students will have some examples to refer to if they are finishing the assignment at home. Each assignment is given a letter grade and is averaged for an assignment grade. I have found that the students will do a better job if they know their assignment will be graded. *(Grade 6)*

(38)   The fourth graders have two assignments in math each week to be completed at home. The third graders have one and perhaps two a week to be completed at home. I check each paper the next day, score it, and return it to the child with comments. I do not record the score unless the child is having difficulty; in that case I want to keep close check on his or her progress. Often a concept has to be retaught and retaught for certain children. *(Grades 3-4)*

(55)   I give homework two times per week for all grades other than first grade. All homework is corrected and returned to the children. If homework is satisfactory, nothing further is done with it. If it is unsatisfactory, the student is given help and asked to correct it. I give children two days to complete their homework. If a child consistently ignores the assignments I look for the reasons. The children are not given a letter grade in the grade book for each assignment. I merely give a grade based on completing and returning assignments for the entire marking period. Many children, believe it or not, beg for homework. A student's responsibility towards homework is considered at report card marking time.
(Math Lab Teacher, Grades 1-5)

(65)   My students have mathematics homework every night except for Friday night. However, work that is incomplete during the week is to be completed over the weekend. If a student

mastered a skill in the classroom, the assignment was adjusted for him or her. To reinforce mastered skills, I give able students challenging problems or activities as homework. Homework allows parents to see what their child is learning and the progress he or she is making. *(Grade 6)*

Exercises for Question 15b

1. List the reasons given by the respondents for giving assignments to be completed outside of class. What additional reasons can you give?

2. What is or would be your policy on assigning homework to be completed outside of class? In your response, indicate the grade level, type of assignments, number of assignments per week, and the amount of time an average student will have to spend on the assignment at home.

3. How would you score assignments completed outside of class, and what use would you make of the scores?

4. In an attempt to encourage students to do their assignments, a teacher might record that a student did an assignment without looking at how the student did on the assignment. How meaningful is this practice? Explain.

5. Give reasons for beginning an assignment in class that is to be completed outside of class. How often should this be done? Explain.

6. Compare and contrast Teacher 55's policy on what is done with students' homework with that of Teacher 33's. Which policy do you prefer? Explain.

7. Should a school district have a policy on assigning homework to students? Explain. If so, what should such a policy be?

8. **Project.** Read the article "Teaching: Using a Textbook Effectively" by Tommie West in the October 1982 issue of the *Arithmetic Teacher*. Critique the author's comments on homework.

Grouping Students

Question 16a: Why do you group students?

Teacher Responses

(12) I group to better assess the continuing needs of the children, to give more individual attention, and to establish a rapport with students so I can answer their questions and build up their confidence in the area of mathematics. *(Grade 1)*

(14) I group so that I can give a slower and more expanded treatment of a topic for slower students; for example, an extensive unit on fractions may use fraction bar manipulatives and worksheets. I also group so that better students can be provided more exposure to enrichment topics and a certain amount of acceleration, and so that I can better manage the games and manipulatives used for instruction. *(Grade 5)*

(16) The rationale for grouping arises from two elements, namely, differing student needs and different ability and performance levels in students. Some students require daily support and explanation while others may work quite well in a tutorial setting. The student with advanced skills should be challenged while the student with learning problems has other needs. It is difficult to meet individual needs in a program that has advanced students and the so-called average learner in one lock-step group. *(Grade 6)*

(17) I group so as to not waste the learning time of students who have already mastered a concept or of those who are not prepared with the necessary skills to understand a particular concept. On a classwide basis, the strong math students are ready and anxious to answer all of the questions or they become too bored to answer. However, in smaller skill groups, each student is at approximately the same level of understanding, is given more time to do his or her own thinking, is less concerned about making an error, and becomes highly enthusiastic about a math discovery that is new to him or her. As a teacher I can better zero in on a concept in a smaller group. I can better keep the attention of the members of the group and stay on top of them until a concept is well understood and mastered. *(Grade 6)*

(22) I want to use the best plan for my students and for me this means teaching small groups. This insures better student understanding and achievement. Having small groups helps the advanced student, the slow learner, and students who missed out because of illness and absence. It also helps me determine the nature of weaknesses. *(Grade 6)*

(47) The students in my class have many different abilities, ranging from a boy with an IQ of 150 to a boy who does not qualify for any school program. (This latter boy is known as a gray area child.) As you can see, the capabilities of these children are expansive; therefore, I felt it necessary to cater a program to their needs. *(Grade 3)*

Exercises for Question 16a

1. List the reasons that the respondents give for grouping and the reasons that the respondents give to Question 17a for not grouping. Are there some reasons that are found in both lists? Why might this be the case? Give your position on grouping and support it.

2. Teacher 17 suggests that, in grouping, the student "is given more time to do his or her thinking" and "is less concerned about making an error." Do you agree or disagree with each of these statements? Explain.

3. Teachers 12 and 22 imply that grouping allows them to know more about problems that a specific student may be having. Give reasons why this may or may not be the case.

4. This statement is made in the conclusion of the bulletin mentioned in Exercise 5: "The implications of this review of research are varied, but one thing does seem clear. No rigid model of classroom organization--group, whole-class, or otherwise--can guarantee the best setting for learning mathematics. In the end, it is the teacher, with the freedom to match teaching strategies with children's needs, who determines the quality of learning in the classroom." What would be your "model of classroom organization," taking into consideration this quote and the responses to Questions 16a and 17a? (See Exercise 1.)

5. **Project.** Read the bulletin "Grouping for Elementary School Mathematics" in *Research Within Reach: Elementary School Mathematics* (1). Summarize the recommendations that appear in this bulletin for intra-class grouping. Also, summarize what the research says about forming groups based on general ability or mathematics achievement. How has this bulletin affected your thinking on grouping?

Question 16b: When do you group students?

Teacher Responses

(4)   My program is individualized. (Is this an absence of groups or is it twenty-six groups?) I do group occasionally when several children are ready to begin a module or when several are experiencing the same difficulty. *(Grade 1)*

(7)   When a few students are having difficulty with a concept and the rest of the class is doing fine, I pull out the few and do additional manipulative activities until they are more sure of the concept. *(Grade 5)*

(17) On the first full day of class in early September, each student begins at exactly the same point, that is, taking our textbook publisher's test on whole number concepts. If a student does not become bogged down with serious weaknesses in whole number work, he or she moves on to the next tests in decimals and fractions, etc., until a seriously weak area presents itself. Meanwhile, as the tests are checked each evening, the student is assigned textbook pages for homework related to the errors made on the tests. In most cases the student with eighty percent or higher (in some cases, after I analyze the type of errors made, with seventy-five percent or higher) is able to continue with the test-taking.

After approximately two weeks of such completely individualized tests and assignments, the students tend to fall into groups--a multiplication fact group, a multiplication process group, a division group, etc., and move along with group assignments. On the other hand, a half-dozen talented math students end up at quite distant individualized areas of competence. These students may remain at an individualized textbook pace for the remainder of the year, but may be grouped for special research assignments, instruction on (or practicing of) the game Equations, evaluation of math and science filmstrips, etc. A large proportion of the class may begin a major math idea such as fractions or decimals together.

However, before fractions can be done, the whole-number division group may have to go on to more specialized assignments (such as exponents or geometry concepts) while the whole number multiplication group catches up. *(Grade 6)*

(35) In our math series, each chapter is set up for basic, average, and enrichment groups. Each chapter has pretests, which enables me to assign each student to a group for that chapter. Some students change groups for each chapter. I also group when there is some math work that is not in the text. *(Grade 6)*

(41) In our seventh grade, two groups are formed at the beginning of the year, namely, accelerated pre-algebra and the regular group. At mid-year, an additional group is formed for remedial work. Also, occasionally there are students who have almost no skills and they would make up a fourth group. *(Grade 7)*

(50) I have two groups, each in a different textbook. After an early screening process, average and above average students are in one book and the others in another. *(Grades 4-5)*

Exercises for Question 16b

1. Make a list of instances when the respondents group. Can you add to this list?

2. A fourth grade teacher says, "I normally group when I am teaching computational skills. This is because the children are best able to help each other with these skills, which then allows me to give some instruction to a specific group. When I am teaching concepts that need a lot of presentation time, such as geometry and measurement, I find it not too meaningful to group because of the little time remaining in the class period." Critique this teacher's policy on when groups are formed.

3. The respondents vary in their grouping policies. Some group occasionally when the need arises, and then the groups are disbanded when the need is no longer there. Others form fixed groups for the whole year, and yet others form new groups just

before the start of a new unit based on a pretest. What are the advantages and disadvantages of each policy? What is or will be your policy?

4. Teacher 50 has two groups with each group using a different textbook. Why would a teacher want to use a different textbook with each group? Would you? Explain.

5. **Project.** Teacher 4 runs an individualized program that appears to be self-paced. Write a summary of the research on self-paced instruction that is given in the section "Self-Paced Instruction" in the bulletin "Learning Elementary School Mathematics: Individual Styles and Individual Needs" in *Research Within Reach: Elementary School Mathematics* (1).

Question 16c: How do you decide on the number of groups and on which students belong to each group?

Teacher Responses

(23) The number of groups I have depends on the class. I have a very social class this year but also very immature. Smaller groups work best with these children. When forming these groups, I try to group children of different skill levels. *(Grade 2)*

(34) The number of groups depends on the concept or skill involved. For instance, Group 1 may be working on four- and five-digit addition, Group 2 on two- and three-digit addition, while Group 3 may still be having trouble learning their addition facts. The students are given a weekly mastery test on what they are studying. If they achieve a score of seventy-five percent, they move to the next concept or skill. *(Grade 4)*

(47) Time unfortunately dictates the number of groups I have. In an hour period I am able to work with only three groups, allowing them 20 minutes of my time and 40 minutes of work time. In determining the placement of students, I give at the beginning of the year a combination test of second, third, and fourth grade skills. From this I get a tentative idea of how to place them. Then I wait until a good month of school passes to see the study habits and eagerness of each student. *(Grade 3)*

(53) I give diagnostic tests in September to determine who belongs where. I try to keep it to two groups. Very low ability students go to a supporting teacher, that is, a learning specialist or a teacher of emotionally impaired children. *(Grade 6)*

(65) At the beginning of the school year I give the entire class the Stanford Diagnostic Mathematics Test. This test gives me some information on the concepts and computational skills that the students have acquired. I form initial groups using these scores, class performance, and scores on tests that I have constructed. Grouping usually begins in mid-October. This

allows the first six weeks of school to be used for review and total group instruction. The deficiencies or strengths of students become very apparent during this period of time. *(Grade 6)*

Exercises for Question 16c

1. Discuss the influence that each of the following should have in forming groups by "achievement" levels: student's behavior characteristics, student's preference, student's attitude, and parent's preference.

2. Teacher 47 does not have time to work with more than three permanent groups because of the amount of time in the class period. This teacher must believe that you can spread yourself too thin by having too many groups. What is the maximum number? Explain. Does your answer depend on whether the groups are fixed groups formed for the whole year or flexible groups formed for specific concepts or skills? Explain.

3. Teacher 23 has children of different skill levels within each group. What are the advantages and disadvantages of this method of grouping? Does grade level make a difference?

4. Teachers 47 and 65 begin the process of forming fixed groups by giving a diagnostic test at the outset of the school year. They then wait from four to six weeks before deciding on the composition of each group. How important is it to have this waiting time before making this decision? Explain.

5. What role should a student's records from previous years play in determining the group into which a student should be placed? Explain. Which of these records would you use?

6. **Project.** Visit a mathematics classroom where some form of grouping takes place. Determine the method of grouping from the teacher and then observe it in action for a few class meetings. Describe and evaluate what you observed.

Question 16d: Do you allow a student to move from one group to another, and under what conditions is this done?

Teacher Responses

(9)   Yes, a student is allowed to move from a lower group to a higher group if he or she shows the skills needed. However, this doesn't happen very often, the main reason being that the higher group has been making rapid progress throughout the year. Thus, even though the student has been moving rapidly in the lower group, he or she has missed too much of the higher group's work. What usually happens is that a new group is created. *(Grade 5)*

(17)   Every student is highly encouraged, urged, cajoled, bribed, and pressured to move on to his or her highest level. (There is presently the strong possibility that two boys and one girl may be well prepared for Algebra I with ninth graders next year.) It is a relatively easy task to move from one group to another during the first few months of the school year because everyone starts off with the same series of speed drills, diagnostic tests, etc. By mid-year, the spread between the three major groups is so great that only some unusual motivating forces would affect the grouping. However, it has occurred in the past several weeks, with two boys showing dramatic improvement and moving from the individualized low group to the average group; they are managing to keep up with the assignments. *(Grade 6)*

(20)   Yes, a student in my special help group may move back into the regular group once the student has mastered the concept that has just been taught. When a new concept is to be taught, new groups may form. Some students need additional help with each concept while others just have trouble with a new concept once in a while.   *(Grade 4)*

(47) Before I place a child into a higher or lower group, I have a conference with him or her. If in a lower group, the child most certainly can be placed in a higher group, depending upon test results, daily papers, a willingness to work, and study habits. It is very rare that I let a child move down from a group. If a child is not working well in a higher group, I have a conference first with the child and then the parent. We determine the problem and then attempt to solve it. The only time that I will move a child down is when, after these conferences, his or her work habits have not improved. *(Grade 3)*

Exercises for Question 16d

1. Teachers 9 and 17 give reasons why it is difficult for a student to move from a lower group to a higher group. What are some ways to handle this problem?

2. Neither Teacher 9 nor 17 mentions moving a student from a higher group to a lower group. Teacher 47 does mention this but says that it is rarely done. What are some problems with a student moving from a higher group to a lower group? What are some problems with keeping a student in a higher group when the student does not seem to be able to handle the work?

3. Is letting a student get "locked" into a group at a particular level a serious shortcoming of having fixed groups? Explain.

Question 16e: How do you work with each group, and what do you have the other groups do while you are working with a particular group?

Teacher Responses

(9) If I have three groups, I will try to meet with two of them on one day while the third group works independently. If I have two groups, one group does a written assignment while I'm teaching the other group. I will sometimes have students work together, if it's a small group, while I'm teaching another one. The group not receiving my instruction has access to the computer and this has worked well. *(Grade 5)*

(16) The top math group meets three days a week: Monday, Wednesday, and Friday. During these sessions individual problems are reviewed. This provides help for those who need it, pre-exposure for those who may not have reached that point, and review for those who have passed that point. The second and third groups work at a fixed pace and meet daily for explanation and review of concepts. While one math group is working, the remaining students may work on any content area they choose. *(Grade 6)*

(22) The main group usually works independently after a new concept has been taught, while I work directly with the special help group. The children in the main group write their names on the board in numerical order if they need teacher help. I make time to lend assistance. Any other math groups that I might have will be working at math, reading, English, spelling, social studies, health, etc. I carefully write daily assignments on the board and number them as to order of importance. *(Grade 6)*

(31) I usually try to work with two of the three groups each day. The third group would be working independently on follow-up exercises. If a child needs help when I am not available, he or she may seek help from another child and may cross groupings

to do so. I try to plan so that the groups who are not working with me are prepared, either the day before or through brief instruction at the beginning of the period, to carry on without me. At times I may appoint a child from another group as a "teacher" to help out when needed. *(Grade 4)*

(32) I have three groups. The highest ability group works independently from assignment charts. Students in this group complete a worksheet or textbook page, check their work, and proceed to the next assignment. I help as requested and check their work nightly, noting their progress and need for instruction. The other two groups work with me daily. I meet the lower ability students first to check yesterday's work, introduce a new concept, and practice the associated skill. They then work on their assignment and I turn my attention to the average ability group. This group has been working on an assignment while I was working with the lowest ability group. I then check their work, introduce new work, and give them some drill activity. *(Grade 3)*

(34) Each group works with me separately. If it is a small group (five or six students), we meet at a large round table. Here we go over the concept. I show each student where mistakes are being made. We work on practice problems together as a group, letting each student take his or her turn explaining a problem. If the group is large, the students remain at their seats while I explain the concept and common mistakes and do practice problems on the board. Students are given a chance to work and explain a practice problem on the board. Meanwhile, the other groups are working on other assignments at their seats. *(Grade 4)*

(45) There may be three to six skill groups initially. During a fifty-minute period I can cover two groups. Cooperation from students is essential. I provide each group with a particular review or practice sheet (or mini-project), which I explain as I pass them out. All students are expected to work while I am involved exclusively with one group. I have checking sheets ready as well as extra puzzles and perhaps a teaching filmstrip or challenge sheets. I may also have one or two student assistants within a class who help with checking or simple explanations. *(Grades 3-4)*

(47) I see my groups in twenty-minute segments. My high group has a unit-by-unit assignment sheet. These students work independently until after I have worked with the other two groups. I see the high group last because their work habits and attention span are much better. I begin the hour with my middle group by giving them a skill lesson and then an assignment. Next I move to my low group, which is working on problems off the board based on the previous day's concept. This is usually about ten problems, which we check together orally. Then I give them their skills and a short assignment. From here I move to the high group, introducing new concepts and doing problems orally. *(Grade 3)*

(57) The classroom has an instruction area, a seatwork area, and a math center area. While the teacher gives instruction to one group, another group is doing seatwork on previously explained concepts, and the third group is working on reinforcement activities or on enjoyment activities at the center. (Students are grouped on behavior characteristics, not on achievement or ability.) Then the groups switch and switch again. Each student has instruction, seatwork, and work at the center every day. Students tutor each other when I am instructing another group. *(Grade 5)*

(65) Each skill group sits together and a group leader is assigned by the teacher. A typical lesson would have Skill Group A working independently on practice or review sheets or on text pages; Skill Group B playing an assigned drill game and doing some independent practice; and Skill Group C working on developing a new concept or computational skill with the teacher. Each session lasts about twenty minutes; then the group rotates to its next activity and the teacher begins work with a different group. At this point Group C would work independently on skill practice; Group B would work with the teacher; and Group A would use games and skill sheets. The variety of activities keeps interest and motivation high, which allows the teacher to work with three small groups during the hour. *(Grade 6)*

Exercises for Question 16e

1. Read the responses and then give your answer to the question.

2. Consider the times during the week when Teachers 9, 16, 32, and 47 meet with each of their groups. Rank these teachers' meeting plans according to your preference. Support your rankings.

3. Teacher 65 chooses a "skill leader" for a group from within that group. What might be the role of this leader? Would you have such a leader? Explain.

4. Teachers 9 and 31 mention having students help each other either within a group or across groups while they work with another group. What are the advantages and disadvantages of doing this? What rules would you have for students working together?

5. Teachers 16 and 22 allow the students in a group they are not working with to work on any subject they choose. Would you allow your students to do this? Explain.

6. Teacher 57, a fifth grade teacher, organizes the classroom into three distinct areas: an instruction area, a seatwork area, and a math center area. Each of her three groups cycle through each area every day. Comment on this plan.

7. Teachers 16, 32, and 47 comment on how they work with the high ability math group. How much instruction time should a teacher give to this group? Explain.

Not Grouping Students

Question 17a: Why do you not group students?

Teacher Responses

(5) I have been successful working with the entire class. I am able to devote more time to the introduction of skills and I am more effective because of this. Also, it is easier for me to monitor the use of manipulative aids. *(Grade 1)*

(18) At the seventh and eighth grade levels, we have placed the top fifteen percent of our students in advanced classes. The very low levels are placed in resource rooms. Students who did not attain the necessary skills the previous year are often retained in that math class. Therefore, the students in a regular math class are already grouped to a degree. Within my own class, I prefer the class to be structured as a single group. I have done some individualization, but I find it difficult to be effective because of the text we have and the curriculum I cover. *(Grades 7-8)*

(19) I do not believe that grouping is the best idea at this level. Students learn as much or more from their peers as they do from us. Many students will find that they suddenly like a

subject and will improve rapidly. If they are placed in a low ability group, very few ever escape to a regular group. *(Grades 7-8)*

(30) Our math periods are thirty-eight minutes, which does not allow for grouping in our program. *(Grades 5-6)*

(33) I have tried grouping and have not been successful. Too many students need me at the same time. Their independent study skills are poor and they do not work well on their own. *(Grade 6)*

(40) The CSMP elementary school math program is intended to be taught to the whole class. Individual differences are met within the lesson, and mastery is not expected before going on to the next concept. The spiral approach insures review and expansion when the concept is presented again. The written work has been developed to meet all levels; therefore, the children can work at their own rates. *(Grade 2)*

(42) I am opposed to the psychological impact on the children when the teacher obviously labels students as "better than" or "inferior to." *(Grades 5-6)*

(74) Right now I have three groups in reading, three in spelling, and the added responsibilities of teaching science, mathematics, social studies, and language arts. *There is not enough preparation time in the day* for me to group in mathematics as well! If a student is having difficulties, I work with him or her before, during, or after school. *(Grade 6)*

Exercises for Question 17a

1. List the reasons that the respondents give for not grouping and the reasons which the respondents give to Question 16a for grouping. Are there some reasons that are found in both lists? Why might that be the case? Give your position and support it.

2. Do you agree with Teacher 42 that it is best not to group because of the psychological impact on children? Explain.

3. Is Teacher 74's reason for not grouping a valid one in your opinion? Explain. If you can't group in all your subjects, in which ones would you group? Why?

4. Do you agree with Teacher 19 that, in grouping, students suffer by not having the opportunity to learn from all their peers? Explain.

5. Critique the response of Teacher 33.

6. **Project.** Read the article "One Point of View: Labels, Labels, Labels" by Shirley Frye in the December 1977 issue of the *Arithmetic Teacher*. How has this article affected your thinking on the forming of fixed or flexible groups?

Question 17b: How do you manage the different levels of achievement in your classroom without grouping students?

Teacher Responses

(1)   The more capable students are usually given extra problems or an assignment that is more advanced. The average or slower student is not expected to accomplish as much. My better students also assist the slower students and many times are successful in getting them to master skills. *(Grades 1-5)*

(15)   Students with math deficiencies are recommended for a tutorial program, which is a special program set up by the parent-teacher coordinator. Students who have a very low achievement level in regular math are referred to special education teachers. I make myself available two or three times per week after school to those students who need extra help. *(Grade 6)*

(20)   I manage the different levels by providing supplemental material for both higher and lower achievers. I have file folders of activities that are done at stations and include work on geometry, measurement, the metric system, problem solving, numeration, and computers. I expand on the concepts in the fourth grade rather than pushing my accelerated students into the fifth grade book.   For my low achievers, motivating spirit masters, repetition, and games help them master basic addition, subtraction, multiplication, and division facts. Math is fun! *(Grade 4)*

(30)   I try to help individuals who are having difficulty during the last 10-15 minutes of class time. When necessary I have a Lunch Club, during which time I will help anyone who desires it. I usually make the day and place known in advance and attendance is voluntary. On occasion I will specifically request or sometimes require a student's participation.   They are

usually more than willing to attend if they need help. I also have set up some teams (two students per team) for tutoring. This also takes place at lunch time. *(Grades 5-6)*

(36) In addition to CSMP worksheets of varying difficulty, I have a math interest center and a microcomputer in my room. Both of these can be used to provide more challenging work for superior students and remedial work for those who need it. The one-star worksheets are usually easy enough so that all students can be successful. The two-star sheets are harder, but many students can do them with ease. I do not expect all students to accomplish the same amount of work. *(Grade 3)*

(44) After a discussion in which the brighter and average students have already been involved, I coax the slower students to answer pointed questions similar to the ones already answered. This gives them a feeling of accomplishment and reviews the idea at the same time. However, you must be willing to wait, for they may take as long as half a minute to a minute to answer. I build their self-confidence by making comments such as "You can do it." They eventually come around. When we work on worksheets or workbooks, I concentrate my attention on those who are slower and try to help them see how to do it. *(Grades 1-5)*

(71) I manage the different levels of achievement by presenting each new concept and skill in any given number of methods, by very thorough reinforcement activities, by partnership help among students, and by individual help. *(Grade 3)*

Exercises for Question 17b

1. How do the respondents manage the different levels of achievement of their students?

2. Do the responses to this question, taken as a group, indicate that the needs of all achievement levels are being met? Explain.

3. How do you think the slower students of Teacher 44 feel about being questioned in the manner described?

4. The responses of Teachers 15 and 30 focus only on how they manage the achievement of slower students. They say nothing about their top students. Do you think that meeting the needs of top students is a low priority item with many teachers? If so, why?

5. How important is it for a teacher, in teaching the whole class, to explain and discuss a concept until the lowest achiever in the class has an excellent chance to understand it? Explain. If you feel it's appropriate, how can you keep the students who understand ideas quickly from losing their motivation for mathematics?

6. How appropriate is it for a teacher, when teaching the whole class, to occasionally give examples or extensions of the content that will challenge the very best students but most likely will be very confusing to many other students? Explain. If you feel it's appropriate to do this, how can you lessen the fears of the other students?

7. One way to manage the different levels of achievement in your classroom is through differentiated assignments. Teachers 1, 20, and 36 do this. Can you give ways in which this can be done so that students will not be explicitly labelled as low, average, or high achievers?

8. **Project.** Read the article "CSMP: A New Alternative in Elementary School Mathematics" by Ernest Woodward in the February 1980 issue of the *Arithmetic Teacher*. Write a review of this article as if you were writing for a teachers' journal, your objective being to inform teachers and to encourage them to read the article.

Helping Students
Who Lack Prerequisites

Question 18:   When a student has difficulty with a concept or skill due to a lack of prerequisite knowledge, how do you provide for this student's needs?

Teacher Responses

(3)   Often I will tutor such a student during the lunch hour. I recently received a new student who had not had rounding off and estimating. I gave individual attention to her and also had her take her book home to do some work. I am still in the process of checking her occasionally to see if her understanding has improved. Reviewing this concept a few minutes with the entire class from time to time is also helpful for such a student. The support of the class to overcome deficiencies due to lack of prerequisite knowledge is a morale booster for the deficient student. Sometimes I arrange for peer tutoring, but I am very careful about how this is done. I hope in the future to have more peer tutoring than I have found possible so far. *(Grades 4-5)*

(13)   Providing for a lack of prerequisite skills is not always easy nor do I always follow the same pattern. Some approaches I use are to allow students to work together, to give time on my

part to the student, to review with the entire class for the individual student's benefit, to provide after-school time or extra skill sheets, and to limit somewhat the concentration on current daily work. *(Grades 7-8)*

(17)   I help such students after group instruction is given or when a large number of students are at band and strings on Tuesday and Thursday from 2-2:45 P.M. Unfortunately, two of the weaker math students are also in band. All students, however, know that I am also available and very willing to give explanations and help during noon recess periods and sometimes during another subject period if the child is ahead in that area.

I help such students after group instruction is given or when a

If the student has basic ability but is weak in several math skills, he or she is referred to our general education resource teacher program. If the missing prerequisite knowledge is basic multiplication or division facts, the parents are asked to help at home and the student is given computer time to work with speed drills that I have programmed. The computer helps also as a motivating force for pure, concentrated effort in memorizing the facts. If the problem is more severe and the student is not too cooperative about staying on task, I have suggested outside tutoring with some excellent results.
(Grade 6)

(19)   I leave the last ten to fifteen minutes of class for students to work on their assignment. It is during this time that I can work with the students who are experiencing difficulty. If students want extra help, I will work with them after school.
(Grades 7-8)

(22)   If prerequisite knowledge is weak or lacking, I begin instruction at that level. This necessitates a great deal of one-to-one teaching but enables me to identify instantly the nature of the difficulty. I have a knack for clearing up difficulties very quickly with one-to-one instruction. However, please note that I teach a self-contained classroom. Therefore, children are occupied with various other assignments and structured activities while I work with the individual or with small groups. The larger the class, the more difficult it is to find time for all who need one-to-one attention every day. *(Grade 6)*

(25)   At the third grade level, a prerequisite knowledge that can cause real problems is a lack of knowledge of the basic addition and subtraction facts. There isn't time to go back and reteach all of these and also teach memorization of multiplication facts. Generally, those students who have not picked up these facts or at least a method of obtaining them (i.e., counting on fingers, using a ruler-number line, drawing pictures, etc.) are those few students who are learning disabled or low achievers. I then encourage these students to use manipulative aids and actively instruct them in their use. My rationale is that if they have not yet learned these facts, they probably never will; you might as well acknowledge this, show them how to get around it, and move ahead to teach the addition and subtraction process and problem solving. I don't believe in holding a child back from learning higher level mathematical processes simply because he or she has to use a ruler to subtract. I don't encourage the use of such aids, but I do accept them for some children. *(Grade 3)*

(34)   I find where the difficulty lies. Then I hunt up materials such as reproducible masters, math workbooks or textbooks, games, puzzles, etc. that deal with this skill. I work individually with the students, check their work with them, and assign new tasks for them to do. *(Grade 4)*

(36)   With the spiral approach of the CSMP elementary school program, there is frequent review and an opportunity to reteach prerequisite skills. Each unit builds upon past experiences and provides an opportunity to ask easy questions to guide the less able students. When I check work I make note of problems that seem to be troublesome to several students. I make sure that I include those problems when that topic is discussed again. *(Grade 3)*

(52)   When a student has difficulty with a concept or skill due to a lack of prerequisite knowledge, I work individually with the student or with small groups doing some background work using a variety of material. I also have a trained math laboratory aide who comes in and takes the child or small groups (no more than four) into the lab to work on that particular skill. I do the planning for these sessions. *(Grades 4-5)*

(69)   While the class is working on an assignment, I individually call the children who are having difficulty up to my desk. The child sits alongside me and we work together. I introduce new ideas and skills to these children along with the rest of the class since this new material might add insight to help them over their difficulties.   *(Grade 3)*

Exercises for Question 18

1.   List the practices given by the respondents in answering this question. How would you answer the question?

2.   Do you agree with Teachers 3 and 13 that it is helpful at times to review a prerequisite skill with the whole class for the benefit of a few? Explain. How could this be done so as to lessen the boredom of students who don't need this review?

3.   Teachers 17 and 19 indicate that students have the option of receiving extra help from them outside of the mathematics class period. Under what circumstances should a teacher encourage students who lack prerequisites to receive extra help from him or her outside of classroom hours? How strong should this encouragement be?

4.   Read the response of Teacher 25 and comment on her philosophy of helping her students "get around" the weaknesses mentioned so that they can learn the process being presented and develop problem solving skills. Would you have this as a general philosophy? Explain.

5.   What role can manipulatives play in remediation? Would their role change depending on grade level? Explain.

6.   Should a teacher involve the student in planning a program of remediation to meet the student's needs? Explain. If you have done this, what have been your experiences?

7.   **Project.** Read the bulletin "Unlocking the Mind of a Child: Teaching for Remediation in Mathematics" from *Research Within Reach: Elementary School Mathematics* (1). What impact has this bulletin had on your thinking about remediation?

Providing for the Academically Talented

Question 19: How do you provide for the needs of the student who is academically talented in mathematics?

Teacher Responses

(4) These students can proceed at their own level and pace. I give them a lot of supplemental work and special activities requiring application of acquired skills. When it is obvious that the child has mastered all concepts and skills and can apply them to specific tasks, then I let him or her begin the second grade book. I have first graders who go beyond the middle of the second grade book. One year I had a multi-age class (grades one through three) in which second graders whom I previously had in first grade also finished the third grade book. *(Grade 1)*

(10) Our school has been exceptionally good about cross-grade grouping. I once had a child who could do fifth grade math in the third grade. The fifth grade teacher was kind enough to take this student for math. She also gave me fifth grade worksheets that were applicable to skills this student should learn. Our math objectives were helpful in this situation. *(Grades 3-4)*

(14)   This student is placed in a group of the best students in my class. This group covers textbook material thoroughly and quickly and is provided with every enrichment activity I can find and fit in. *(Grade 5)*

(15)   Special attention is given to these students. I use another textbook with them that has been carefully selected by a special book committee. Supplementary problems are included for each unit and additional enrichment worksheets are available in the teacher's manual. We also make use of challenging math games, puzzles, etc. *(Grade 6)*

(17)   Among other things, I use the problems from old copies of the State Mathematics Competition. The students enjoy these. *(Grade 6)*

(20)   I have activities in supplemental folders that the students may do to broaden their knowledge. We work with graphing, string art, geometric art designs, individual math projects, chess tournaments, etc. There are always challenging activities available for these youngsters. They really enjoy them and may work independently or with a friend. *(Grade 4)*

(26)   I like to believe all my students are academically talented. I always try to teach to the top end of their ability. Problem selection ranges from easy to difficult on each assigment. *(Grade 8)*

(33)   I have a number of challenging activities in the classroom for the talented student to pursue. We subscribe to *Scholastic Math Magazine* which comes twice a month. This magazine provides an interesting variety of activities and the students like it. *(Grade 6)*

(36)   These students always do the four-star worksheets in the CSMP workbook, which are the most advanced worksheets. I have programs for a microcomputer that are more challenging and I include some activities in the math center that are more difficult. *(Grade 3)*

(42)   Both Questions 19 and 20 can be answered with one word: computer. I have many programs for the talented. The academically deficient student most often lacks mastery of basic facts. The incredible power of the computer to motivate usually clears this up in short order. Sometimes, the computer handles both talented and deficient students simultaneously. Recently, I saw a group of students gathered around the computer after school had been dismissed. They were involved with a program that required the answer to simple multiplication facts. When I asked what they were doing, the response was, "We're running Andy's program." Andy is talented and had written the program; the others could use the practice. Interestingly enough, it did not occur to the members of the group that they were doing math. I regard teaching children to program the computer as a good application for the talented, though not necessarily confined to that group. *(Grades 5-6)*

(50)   I have many materials for challenging math students. They are required to try materials from different areas in the math center per card marking. I have a check-off record keeping system. I attend math workshops and belong to a professional mathematics organization. I subscribe to the *Arithmetic Teacher* and *Games Magazine. (Grades 4-5)*

(56)   If I have a child who is academically talented in mathematics, I will research professional magazines, catalogs listing supplemental math materials, or teacher stores to purchase material for the child. One year I had a first grade child who wouldn't read but just loved math. In my search I discovered a company that sold story problem workbooks. This child wanted to work in the workbook, which was enough incentive to start to read. By the end of the second grade, this young man and I were doing fourth grade math and reading assignments. *(Grades 1-3)*

(65)   I provide a "Challenge Chart," which lists ideas that a student could pursue independently. For example:
1. Design a chart to show the class the differences and similarities between the Egyptian and Roman numeral systems.
2. Create a set of five story problems that are to be solved by members of your mathematics group. Try to make them use as many processes as you can in solving them.
3. Take the trundle wheel and any five activity cards pertaining to it and do the work requested.
4. Begin a booklet on geometry. Use the encyclopedia to get background information. *(Grade 6)*

Exercises for Question 19

1. List how the respondents provide for the needs of the student who is academically talented in mathematics. What additional suggestions can you give? Which three items on the list are of most interest to you from the standpoint of a teacher? Explain.

2. Give your description of a student who is academically talented in mathematics.

3. Teacher 4 allows her talented mathematics students to progress through textbooks used at higher grade levels. Many of the other teachers do not have their students do this, but instead provide them with enrichment materials. Which of these two methods do you or would you use? Explain.

4. Give pros and cons of placing one or more of your academically talented students in a math class at a higher grade level, as Teacher 10 does.

5. What are your feelings about using an alternate textbook with talented students as described by Teacher 15 versus just providing these students with more difficult problem assignments?

6. List the sources that the respondents use to find materials for their students who are academically talented in mathematics. What additional sources can you give?

7. How can a school or school district provide for the needs of the academically talented student in mathematics?

8. **Project.** Critique one of the four articles on classroom activities for able students that appear in the February 1981 issue of the *Arithmetic Teacher*.

Providing for the
Academically Deficient

Question 20: How do you provide for the needs of the student who is academically deficient in mathematics?

Teacher Responses

(4) I discuss the deficiency with the parents and give them aids and instruction for helping their child. I may have a parent volunteer work one-to-one with these children. These children are often in the Title I or Academic Support programs and can receive help there. *(Grade 1)*

(9) I take the child at whatever level he or she is at and start from there. This may mean going back to learning basic number facts and place value. In our district, a child with severe deficiencies in math can be referred to a special math skills program. Also, counseling and tutoring may be suggested. *(Grade 5)*

(10) We have an excellent math aide who helps these children. I also work individually with the academically deficient students and use more visual aids with them. I also get material from other teachers who are teaching at the level at which these students are working. On occasion I have capable students helping those who have more difficulty understanding the concepts. *(Grades 3-4)*

(14) This student is placed in a group of similar students. This group does not do everything, but what it does is done thoroughly and carefully until every student has had some success. My most extensive use of manipulative materials is with this group. *(Grade 5)*

(31) Those who are academically deficient present the greatest problem because they need *time*. Frequently, these are the children who lack motivation, and finding a way to interest them concerns me most. I can't say that any one way of doing this has worked. I simply struggle to provide as best I can, much as I would for other children who lack prerequsite knowledge. *(Grade 4)*

(36) These children can usually complete the one-star worksheets in the CSMP workbook. If they still have trouble, I work with them, pointing out things that they missed, or I encourage them to draw arrow pictures or use the minicomputer to figure out their answers. They may also use number lines or blocks, but very few students need them with the CSMP elementary school program. *(Grade 3)*

(52) Academically deficient students work with the average group in mathematics. Because children learn and gain support from each other, I don't believe in putting them in a separate group during the regular class period. My expectations are lower for them. Some of them may not be able to go much beyond the very first stage of each concept, but they have a better attitude toward themselves and tend to try harder. *(Grades 4-5)*

(56) Working with the primary child who is academically deficient in math can be very challenging. I try to keep on hand a wide range of materials for all the various abilities. I also take the class's worksheets and modify them for some children who would feel uncomfortable doing an activity that is different from what the other children are doing. *(Grades 1-3)*

Exercises for Question 20

1. List how the respondents provide for the needs of the student who is academically deficient in mathematics. What additional suggestions can you give?

2. Give your description of a student who is academically deficient in mathematics.

3. What expectations do you or will you have for your students who are academically deficient in mathematics? Is it reasonable to expect that an academically deficient student in mathematics will overcome his or her deficiency? Explain.

4. Contrast the responses of Teachers 14 and 52. Which do you most agree with? Explain.

5. Give some advantages and disadvantages of an academically deficient student working in a lower grade level textbook or in the math class of a lower grade level teacher.

6. How important are manipulatives in helping students who are academically deficient in mathematics? Explain.

7. **Project.** Write a review of the article "Slow or Learning Disabled--Is There a Difference?" in the December 1976 issue of the *Arithmetic Teacher*.

Providing for the Mainstreamed Student

Question 21:   How do you provide for the needs of the student who is being mainstreamed?

Teacher Responses

(12)   Again, my aide is an invaluable asset. I use her as support for the mainstreamed student. *(Grade 1)*

(17)   This is very difficult to do if an emotional problem is hindering the child's progress. I have conferences with the parent at school and over the telephone, with the learning resources teacher, and with the student. There is an ebb and flow to the problem: the student may be cooperating, concentrating, and making progress, then will spend a week or two constantly out of his or her seat and disturbing others. The moment that I complete this question, I shall begin typing contracts for my two mainstreamed students. They will concentrate on their assignments for a half-hour period, take a break to help younger students with computer work in the media center and read them a story, then do general library jobs which they enjoy, and so on. *(Grade 6)*

(30)   I work in close cooperation and am in constant communication with the learning center teacher. If the student has difficulty with a skill, the learning center teacher also works with the student. If the student is emotionally impaired, he or she may remain in my room unless the student is disruptive. Generally, such students need a great deal of reassurance. This question is difficult to answer unless describing particular students since they vary so much. I was talking about specific cases in my answer above. *(Grades 5-6)*

(33)   Presently, I have four students that have been mainstreamed in three different math classes. They work very well with the class and have been doing average and above average work. They are given the same assignments and I have the same expectations for them as for the rest of the class. It has worked very well. *(Grade 6)*

(36)   This has not been a big problem with the CSMP elementary school program. However, children must listen and pay attention. I make sure that I call on all children frequently. I vary the difficulty of the questions asked so that all children can answer correctly. This is easier to do with CSMP than with a traditional program. *(Grade 3)*

(45)   I have had limited experience with mainstreamed students; but, because they were placed by ability rather than age or grade level, I fit them into groups and work with them in the usual manner. *(Grades 3-4)*

(47)   I currently have two students who are being mainstreamed into my room. They are placed in my middle group and receive the same daily instruction as anyone else in the group. One boy has his assignments cut down and he goes to the learning center to complete his assignment. He works much better when there are absolutely no distractions and his questions can be answered immediately at the learning center. The other boy works fine in the middle group and completes his assignments daily. *(Grade 3)*

Exercise for Question 21

1. **Project.** Read the article "Help for Learning Disabled Students in the Mainstream" by Bley and Thornton in the 1982 NCTM Yearbook, *Mathematics for the Middle Grades (5-9)*. Select four intervention techniques that particularly impress you and indicate why.

Special Resource Materials

Question 22a: Do you make use of special mathematics resource materials (games, puzzles, tapes, calculators, microcomputers, etc.)? What do you have available?

Teacher Responses

(3) I make use of many resource materials. I have a wide variety of games, both commercial and teacher made, including strategy games such as checkers, Othello, Rack-O, Connect-Four, and Equations. Other resource materials I use are large-size grids to show missing numbers to stimulate pattern perception, Shapespaper, geoboards, attribute blocks, individual clocks, scales, Cuisenaire rods, metric aids of all kinds including two metric trundle wheels, solid shapes, individual abaci as well as several large ones for classroom demonstration, two old Kresge cash registers, magnetic board, tape drills for basic facts, overhead projector and transparencies, and sixteen calculators. *(Grades 4-5)*

(4) I have over 200 commercial and teacher-made games in manila expanda-file pockets and stored in file cabinets and cupboards. They cover concepts in the first, second, and third grade

curriculum. I can easily pull a game that will reinforce a particular concept or maintain a skill. I have two fifth grade boys who come three times a week for a half-hour each time. They play games with the kids. *(Grade 1)*

(13) Resource materials are a way of expanding the student's awareness of a concept. I allow time weekly or bimonthly to use such materials. Our middle school has use of a math lab in which many of the usual resource materials are kept and presented to all math classes. We also have the benefit of a classroom set of solar cell calculators for math classes and an all-school computer lab. The computer lab is staffed by math and science teachers throughout the day and is available for students in any discipline to use on a sign-up basis. *(Grades 7-8)*

(14) I have a large collection of games and puzzles that I have purchased or made at workshops. I have nearly everything ever offered by our county make-and-take workshops. I have many purchased materials such as Fraction Bars, Base 10 Blocks, Chip Trading, Master Mind, sports math games, etc. I have a calculator and several electronic games such as Quiz Kid. Our media center has a classroom set of calculators and three microcomputers. *(Grade 5)*

(16) Calculators, microcomputers, and other resources are used as aids to the math program. The microcomputers are used for remediation and drill and as a vehicle for teaching thinking skills through programming. Each student is encouraged to bring a calculator to school that may be used for scoring, some story problems, and general math other than daily assignments. *(Grade 6)*

(18) We have approximately fifteen to twenty math filmstrips and cassettes in the building and others in the district. We also own a variety of card games, Master Mind, Equations, Soma puzzles, as well as tangrams, geoboards, metric materials, volume models, cubes, probability kits, and posters. Also, I have a number of related materials made and collected over the past nine years. *(Grades 7-8)*

(31) Yes, I make use of many resource materials. I have games, puzzles, tapes, filmstrips, records, calculators, Cuisenaire rods, tangrams, and many measurement aids. We have some microcomputers in the building. I also have access to a variety of books from which I can produce a large variety of activities. *(Grade 4)*

Exercises for Question 22a

1. What sources for special mathematics resource materials are mentioned by the respondents? What additional sources can you give?

2. What special mathematics resource materials are mentioned by the respondents? What additional sources can you give?

3. A teacher said that "One key to being successful with special mathematics resource material is organization." What are some organizational problems that can be encountered with using these materials and how can they be handled?

4. What are some reasons for teachers not making use of special mathematics resource materials that are available to them? What can be done to help teachers make more use of these materials?

5. **Project.** Write a review of the chapter "The Computer as a Learning Center," which appears in the 1984 NCTM Yearbook, *Computers in Mathematics Education*.

6. **Project.** Read the chapter "Using Games to Teach Fraction Concepts and Skills" by Bright and Harvey in the 1982 NCTM Yearbook, *Mathematics for the Middle Grades (5-9)*. Construct a lesson plan for using a game to reinforce mathematical concepts. In your plan, describe how the game is played and the mathematical concepts that are to be reinforced by playing the game.

Question 22b: When do the students use the special mathematics resource materials?

Teacher Responses

(5)   There are certain times, at least once a week, when the class goes to the math corner and uses the special materials that are located there. Students may also use these materials when their work is completed. *(Grade 1)*

(31)   Puzzles and games are available to the children when they have completed their assigned work. The use of most other materials is incorporated into my lesson plans since their use must be correlated with the plans of other teachers. *(Grade 4)*

(36)   Students use the microcomputer before school, at noon, at recess, and during the day when time permits. Calculators are often used to develop a lesson. I also let students use calculators to check their worksheets from the interest center. Some students use the Little Professor "calculator" for drill and practice. The other games I have are used by the children when they have free time. *(Grade 3)*

(42)   There are three possibilities for the use of microcomputers. First, I assign a given time and program to one or two students. Second, the computer is hooked to a monitor and is used with the entire class. The third time is "free time" use when, for a half-day, a specific student may use the computer whenever he or she has time. On occasion, I will excuse a student from an assignment that can easily be done at home to allow more time at the computer. Students choose to work alone or with a partner. Their turn on the machine is determined by lottery. A "user chart" is posted in the room and when a turn has been taken, the student places a check after his or her name. They have free choice of the program selected since the only ones in the room have been determined by me to have academic value. *(Grades 5-6)*

(44) I use these materials when the lesson calls for them. For example, I use a calculator in a detective story where the emphasis is on logical thinking and not on the calculations. *(Grades 1-5)*

(52) The materials may be checked out of the mathematics laboratory by teachers to use in their classrooms. Each class is scheduled for at least an hour each week when the total class can be taken to the lab. The games and activities can be directed by the teacher and an adult aide. This same scheduled period may be used as the teacher sees fit for individual or small group instruction, usually by a trained aide. *(Grades 4-5)*

Exercises for Question 22b

1. List the times the respondents use their resource materials. What additional possibilities can you give?

2. How strongly would you encourage your students, upon completing the required mathematics class work, to select and work with some special mathematics resource materials that may be located on a math table? What benefits can students gain by doing this? How would you manage this activity?

3. When do the respondents use calculators in their classrooms? When do you or will you use calculators in the classroom? Why don't teachers plan more for their students' use of this tool?

4. Discuss the advantages and disadvantages of having your own special mathematics resource materials versus having such materials housed in a mathematics laboratory where they are available for use by the whole school.

5. **Project.** Write a summary of the bulletin "Calculators in the Classroom" in *Research Within Reach: Elementary School Mathematics* (1).

Finding Time to Give Individual Help

Question 23: When do you find time to give individual help to a student?

Teacher Responses

(7) I have a classroom rule that during the "work" time of the math period, children must remain silent and seated. Each child has a little Tinkertoy flag. If the child needs help, he or she raises the flag on its stand and goes on to another problem that can be worked. This gives me the opportunity to go to each child and provide help. I also remain after school to give help and have some time before school to clear up confusions that exist. *(Grade 5)*

(9) I try to plan one day a week when I do not meet with all my groups for formal teaching. This allows me time to work with individual students either at my desk or by moving around the room. I sometimes pick a star student and tell the students that they can go to him or her for help. *(Grade 5)*

(28) After the daily lesson, fifteen to twenty minutes is provided to work on that day's assignment. I walk around the room to

note trouble areas and provide individual help. Some days I remain at my desk and encourage students to bring their questions up to me. After school dismissal, I am available for one hour and forty-five minutes in the building to help anyone who requests help or needs catching up after being absent. *(Grades 7-8)*

(35)   When the class is working on a math assignment, anyone who needs additional help can come to me for assistance. Also, a study period is provided each afternoon when students may come to me for additional help. *(Grade 6)*

(52)   I almost always give individual help while the groups are working quietly on practice work. Depending on the attitude of the child involved, I sometimes give individual help during recess or during some other break time. *(Grades 4-5)*

(55)   Finding time to work one-to-one with an individual student comes under the category of miracles. It's possible but divine intervention is nearly required. Actually, there are several ways it can be managed. One time to get hold of a child with special needs is when the rest of the group is doing a workbook assignment. Also, I get to school very early in the morning and often have a child come in early--the morning quiet is conducive to giving individual help. Sometimes children come for help during my coordinating period and sometimes during lunch. This about sums it up. Students are always willing to come for extra help so I can usually make some kind of plan for them. *(Math Lab Teacher, Grades 1-5)*

(75)   Throughout the class day I always schedule some quiet time periods where students can choose an activity of their choice. During this time I seek out students, either low achievers or high achievers, who need help with their projects. *(Grade 3)*

Exercises for Question 23

1. List the times at which the respondents give individual help to a student. Can you suggest other times?

2. Give reasons for students being reluctant to seek out individual help from their teacher. How can each of these reluctancies be overcome?

3. What balance should a teacher, such as Teacher 28, maintain between seeking out students who need help and waiting for students to seek out the teacher? Explain.

4. What suggestions can you offer a teacher who, on a given day, does not have the time to give individual help to all the students who need it?

5. How reasonable is it to expect a teacher to be available before or after school to give individual help to a student? Explain. What about during lunch time?

Students Helping Other Students

Question 24: Do you have students help other students with their mathematics lesson? If so, how frequently, in what way, and how has it worked?

Teacher Responses

(6) When many students need my help, I ask some of the more able students to be assistants. Also, after finishing an assignment of practice problems, students can pair off, compare answers, and find mistakes. I often have them work story problems in groups. Discussion is thought-provoking and members of the group often correct each other's thinking. *(Grade 5)*

(8) Students often help others. Since they are in different places in the book and three or four different levels of books are used in the class, most students are able to get *and* give quality help. Children are often very good teachers, and their participation in this activity helps them maintain their skills and feel good about themselves and their accomplishments. *(Grades 3-4)*

(16)   Generally, students are encouraged to help each other in all areas. This helps to foster a group spirit and aids learning as the students discuss the concepts. Through articulation their understanding is reinforced. In some instances a student may relate better or more effectively to another student than to me. *(Grade 6)*

(17)   Yes, but not too frequently since students tend to give away answers too easily. If a student asks for an explanation of a problem just after I have explained it to another youngster, I often request the latter to explain it to the second student using my method. I then ask the second student to re-explain it to me. This triangular chain of explanations has proved very successful. Students who have been absent will usually get an explanation of the material from other students at my request, and are to see me if necessary. Students may also seek help from other students when I'm busy with someone. If it is not too often or too long I seldom interrupt. Often a student accepts personal help better from another student than from me. After checking work after school I'll enter class and say, "Hey Mike, John wrote that 1/4 = 3/12 yesterday, which is great, but he also wrote that 2/3 = 6/12. Will you go out into the hall with him and show him why 2/3 cannot equal 6/12 ?" They'll both love having a legitimate reason for being out of the classroom. *(Grade 6)*

(28)   During the fifteen to twenty minute period that students are working on their assignment, they compare, argue, and defend their particular answers. They gravitate towards each other and know who to ask if they have a question and I can't get to them immediately. I find this very useful because the students encourage each other and catch their mistakes before they fall behind. *(Grades 7-8)*

(45)   Some children respond better to a student helper than to an adult. As soon as I detect a shy and withdrawn low achiever, he or she gets a helper. These two work closely together on class assignments. My low achievers have always gained strength in skill mastery and self-confidence because of this arrangement. *(Grades 3-4)*

(51)   If a child has been absent, I often will have a strong math student explain the missed assignments. Also, after a new concept is presented, I will assign five sample problems and

then check a student in each row for understanding. If these students understand the sample problems and get them all right, they are allowed to move up and down their rows checking and helping with these five problems. *(Grades 2-3)*

(55) Yes, this is helpful under certain conditions. I'll try to explain my point of view. The children who are going to work together must be compatible, and the child doing the helping must be clear about the mission. Also, keep the time span short and stay on the alert, as children confuse giving away answers with helping. Give all levels of students a chance to be in the driver's seat; it's a great ego booster for slower learners. There are times I have children do workbook pages together because I think it improves the lesson. An example of this is the more difficult pages in the workbooks for the CSMP elementary school program. Children are more apt to attempt them if they have someone to work out strategies with. Children do work together in our math laboratory, but with teacher input and supervision. *(Math Lab Teacher, Grades 1-5)*

(67) I feel strongly about children helping each other since this strengthens knowledge for both children involved. Sometimes children will listen better if it's a peer talking rather than a teacher. The frequency of helping depends on the material and the difficulty a child may have in explaining it. *(Grade 4)*

(72) This is done on a voluntary basis only. High achieving students are sometimes taken advantage of by teachers. They are being deprived of other challenges if they are almost always being teachers. When I pair for tutoring, I often pair students who are only a few steps apart in their knowledge. Then it becomes a learning situation for both children. *(Grade 5)*

(81) Yes, children help each other quite frequently. Sometimes they work in pairs, particularly if a new skill is being learned. Another child's explanation is often more helpful to a specific individual than the *repetition* of an explanation by the teacher. *(Grade 3)*

Exercises for Question 24

1. List the benefits given by the respondents for students helping each other with their mathematics lesson. Can you give additional benefits?

2. List the problems given by the respondents in having students help each other with their mathematics lesson. Can you give additional problems? What can the teacher do to minimize these problems?

3. For what purposes do the respondents have students help other students? Can you give additional purposes?

4. Teachers 6, 16, and 28 talk about having students discuss mathematics with each other. What benefits do you see in having students do this?

5. Critique this technique of Teacher 45: "As soon as I detect a shy and withdrawn low achiever, he or she gets a helper."

6. Critique this technique of Teacher 72: "When I pair for tutoring, I often pair students who are only a few steps apart in their knowledge."

7. What statements can a teacher make to students on how to help another student in mathematics?

8. **Project.** Read the article "Children as Teachers--Some Fundamental Operations" by David Clarkson in the October 1975 issue of the *Arithmetic Teacher*. How has this article affected your thinking about the value of students helping other students? Explain.

Teacher Aides and Volunteer Helpers

Question 25: What specific tasks are handled by teacher aides and volunteer helpers during your mathematics lessons? How are they recruited and trained, and how successful have they been?

Teacher Responses

(8) I have no paid aides, only parent volunteers. I have a meeting at the beginning of the year to explain the record keeping system, what the volunteer's function is in the classroom, when to help and when not to, etc. This has worked very well in the past. *(Grades 3-4)*

(15) The specific tasks I give my aide are to check test papers, put away students' math folders, clean the screen on the overhead projector, get supplies from the attendance office (such as paper, pencils, note pads, and attendance forms), record daily absentees, and help with bulletin boards. I just give the aide a written job description and explain what his or her responsibilities are to successfully do the job. *(Grade 6)*

(18) I do not have any teacher aides. I have a student assistant (an eighth grader) who helps check late assignments and some quizzes or tests. He also helps with bulletin boards, cutting letters, etc., and may monitor or give an oral quiz when needed. *(Grades 7-8)*

(24) Each year several high school students volunteer to assist at our school because they know from the past how we appreciate this type of assistance and how useful it can be. They come during their free time (arrangements and scheduling are made) or they may take an independent study class under my supervision. The two high school helpers I had were former students and they know our program well. Senior citizens become familiar with our program by observing classes, asking questions, and gradually working into our system. Parents are always welcome and sometimes give assistance. I also recruit resource helpers by personally contacting people I know. An article done about my classroom inspired other people of the community to volunteer. One parent in the district comes yearly to work with the students on income tax; a social security worker explains the social security process to students; and another parent shows how to figure bowling scores. These are but a few of the ways these wonderful people assist us. *(Grades 3-5)*

(26) I, as do other teachers, have student aides from the high school. We each train our aides and grade them since they are taking an elective high school course that gives them credit for being an aide. The student aides handle the preparation of spirit masters, quiz papers, and worksheets. They also grade some minor quizzes and tests. Aides are selected the previous year and are screened by the supervising teacher based on their attitudes and abilities. *(Grade 8)*

(38) When I have an adult aide, he or she walks around giving individual help after I have taught the lesson. They also work with small groups reinforcing the lesson or even reteaching it. They are trained by me. This system works well.
(Grades 3-4)

(39) The local university sends tutors to help me. They work with all levels of students in the class. *(Grade 7)*

(48) I had a hired aide when my class load was thirty-six. She watched me develop the lesson. Then, as children worked on

their assignment, she was able to use the same method in order to avoid confusion. This is very successful if the aide takes initiative in locating frustrated students. I recruit volunteers by word-of-mouth, from among college students who are prospective teachers, from new parents being given a tour by the principal (they are so impressed they sign up), from mothers of youngsters involved in the pre-school or speech therapy programs at our school, and at curriculum night in early fall. I train the volunteers at a three-hour session at the beginning of the school year and continue to train as I get new learning materials or new teaching ideas. They also train each other. The use of volunteers has been very successful. *(Grades 4-6)*

(51)   Parent volunteers respond to a help-wanted letter at the beginning of the year. I instruct them on how to use the machines, check papers, etc. By having them free me from these tasks, I have more time for gathering and organizing materials and planning. *(Grades 2-3)*

(52)   The math aides help by directing math games and activities, by drilling students in the basic facts using flash cards, by assisting with computational algorithms when a child is having difficulty, and by reading story problems where reading difficulty exists. These aides are screened by other teachers, the principal, and myself. They are trained by me and other resource persons during workshops to work with specific skills using available materials. The program has been extremely successful. It has become more difficult to find aides since most adults who would volunteer their time and enjoy doing so are now employed and are not available to help during school hours. *(Grades 4-5)*

(55)   One aide has been assigned to the math lab for one-half of each day. She has been an aide with our math department for over ten years. She has also had the special training required to teach the CSMP elementary school program. Of the three hours per day she spends in the math lab, fifty percent is spent helping children either individually or in small groups of two or three. The children love her and the help she gives them. Another portion of her time is spent on giving a math diagnostic test to children whose skills we need to know more about. If a parent comes in for an unexpected conference, the aide is able to take the class for me. Children definitely show progress under her tutelage. *(Math Lab Teacher, Grades 1-5)*

Exercises for Question 25

1. List the types of helpers for teachers that are mentioned by the respondents. Can you suggest other types? Which types do you prefer? Explain.

2. List how the respondents recruit teacher aides or volunteer helpers. Can you suggest other ways to recruit these individuals?

3. List how the respondents train teacher aides or volunteer helpers. Can you suggest other training methods?

4. What do the respondents say about their success with using teacher aides and volunteer helpers? Describe how successful your experiences have been in either using teacher aides and volunteer helpers or in being a teacher's helper.

5. Teacher 24 mentions the use of community resource people who come into class to inform her students about their work or to teach them some applications of mathematics. What is your opinion of using these resource people for these purposes? How frequently do you or would you use them? Explain. Why isn't more use made of them?

6. The respondents mention many tasks that the teacher aides and volunteer helpers do. Pick three tasks mentioned by the respondents that would be especially helpful to you and explain why you choose them. What tasks are mentioned by the respondents that you would not have teacher aides or volunteer helpers do? Explain.

Involving Parents in Helping Their Children

Question 26: How do you involve parents in helping their children with mathematics?

Teacher Responses

(3) When parental help is deemed necessary, I write or call the parents and explain my reasons for asking for their help. Usually I ask for support in seeing that the child is provided with the time and a quiet place in which to work, and that the child's work is done before pursuing leisure time activities such as TV or long conversations on the phone. That is the best help a parent can provide. *(Grades 4-5)*

(4) I explain the first grade curriculum to the parents at a grade level meeting early in the year and have handouts available for them. I send home portions of the workbook completed by a student with appropriate comments and suggestions for the parents. Five or six times a year the children take home "math bags" for about a week each time. There is an "idea" book in the bag as well as dice, cards, dominoes, beadlines, and directions for playing many games. There are also sets of addition and subtraction facts. Whenever a child is having

difficulty, I discuss it with the child's parents at a conference. I show them how to help their child and give them appropriate aids. Occasionally I recommend a tutor or a summer session at a nearby school. This might be a good place to insert this item: Sometimes it helps if I can get the parents to see that there is a difference between parroting facts (e.g., $2 + 2 = 4$, $100 + 100 = 200$, $3 \times 3 = 9$) and understanding the concept, being able to put it into writing, and being able to apply it to other situations. Parents hear their children saying all these facts and think they are gifted in the area of math and expect them to have no trouble at all. *(Grade 1)*

(16)   Parents are encouraged to help their children as much as possible. The key word, though, is *help*, not "do for." *(Grade 6)*

(17)   During open house in early October, I explain the math program and request parents to review and drill their sixth graders on the basic facts of addition, subtraction, multiplication, and division. I also request that parents provide them with as many concrete math experiences as possible: measuring length and area, grocery shopping for "best buys," banking, baking, etc. I give students rewards if a note from home said that they had done such practical math work. Parents may also be called during the year to help their child line up numerals in a multiplication or division problem or to help organize problems neatly and space them well on a sheet of paper. When parents are given clear and specific directions, their help can be very effective. *(Grade 6)*

(28)   Many parents find it difficult to help their child who is working in the middle of a chapter. However, the notebook the child brings home contains my lesson and examples to aid with the homework. Many parents are surprised to learn that assignments are given daily. I encourage them to watch for this notebook and look over their child's work. I personally call parents and ask for their follow-up at home to guarantee that the work is getting done and with accuracy. *(Grades 7-8)*

(36)   I explain the math program at the open house in the fall. I give parents a schedule and I also list a number of ways that they can help their child improve. Throughout the year I send letters home explaining what we have been doing at school, what we will be doing, and how parents can help their child at home.

This year I had an extra evening for the parents in which I explained the things that we were doing in the CSMP elementary school program. *(Grade 3)*

(39) I make them aware that students may need more help than we can provide in the classroom and that just by sitting occasionally with a child while he or she is doing homework gives him or her the confidence needed to accomplish the task. *(Grade 7)*

(48) I involve parents by asking for their help via the telephone, particularly when homework is missing or test scores are low. Parents must sign and return end-of-chapter tests. I ask the child to redo missed problems at home with their parents' help. *(Grades 4-6)*

(55) We have some wonderful parents at our school. If I ask a parent who comes for a conference to help his or her child, I am never turned down. What I try to do is have work ready for the parent to take home. I prefer this to just sending it home with the child, as I can explain it better. If the student is doing work from the CSMP elementary school program, I send home more traditional work so as to avoid confusion for the parents. CSMP students can slip back and forth between CSMP and traditional math with ease. If parents cannot get to school, I phone them and then send the work home. One or two contacts with the parent is usually enough to see an improvement in the child's work. If this is not the case, then usually it's a serious gap and requires different measures. At the beginning of each school year, a letter is sent home to all parents describing our math program.   When funds are available we schedule math workshops for parents. Both math rooms (laboratory and regular) have an open door policy. Visitors are always welcome. Parents have a copy of the homework schedule and know when to expect it. Sometimes I request that homework assignments be signed by the parent. *(Math Lab Teacher, Grades 1-5)*

(68) This is difficult to answer because many times the parents of these children have had difficulty with mathematics themselves. I try to give them concrete ways to help develop their child's math skills; examples include grocery shopping, measuring areas at home, keeping track of expenditures, etc. *(Grade 4)*

(70)   I usually ask the parents of students who find math difficult to read the material over with their child so the parent and child can understand together. This is done especially to show parents the new development of some concepts; hence, they will then be in a position to aid their child. *(Grade 4)*

(76)   I encourage parents to reinforce work done well, not to overly pressure the child, to assist when asked, and to take an interest in the child's work. *(Grade 3)*

(79)   I tell parents to help if their child asks for it and if they are able to help. Parents should ask their child if he or she wants their help but should not give help if it is not wanted. *(Grade 8)*

(81)   Based on personal experience with parents, my strongest suggestion is for parents to relax and accept that their child may be having some difficulties with math. I have seen some parents become so upset that they want extra homework every night for their child. The child ends up hating math and becomes very frustrated with himself or herself. Also, if a parent is going to work with his or her child, then it must be when the child and parent are relaxed and ready. Finally, parents should try to relate mathematical concepts to everyday experiences so the child can see the application of skills and concepts and how they relate to his or her life. *(Grade 3)*

(82)   I encourage parents to develop in their child a "mathematical mind." This can be done by encouraging the child to be inquisitive, a problem solver, and logical. In addition, where skills are weak, I give the parents reinforcement activities to use with their child in order to strengthen these skills. *(Grade 3)*

Exercises for Question 26

1. List how the respondents involve parents in helping their children
   with mathematics. Do you disagree with any of their methods?
   Can you suggest additional methods? Are the majority of these
   ways applicable to most subject areas? Explain.

2. A consistent refrain throughout the responses is the importance of
   effective and consistent communication between parents and
   teachers. Give examples of when a teacher should communicate
   with parents about their child. What responsibility does the
   teacher have to initiate this communication? To what length
   should a teacher go to maintain this communication?

3. If a child needs help in mathematics beyond that given by parents
   and teachers, what responsibility does each party have in
   ensuring that the child gets this help?

4. What are the advantages of having parents "sign and return
   end-of-chapter tests," which is the stated policy of Teacher 48?
   Do you or would you have this as your policy? Explain.

5. In regard to parents helping children, Teacher 16 states that "the
   key word, though, is *help*, not 'do for'." What are some
   suggestions that a teacher can give to parents on how to help their
   children?

6. Teacher 81 states that "I have seen some parents become so upset
   that they want extra homework every night for their child. The
   child ends up hating math and becomes very frustrated with
   himself or herself." What would you do if parents of one of your
   students insisted that this be done for their child, yet you believe
   it is not in that child's best interest?

7. How important is it for students to be allowed to take graded tests
   home to show their parents? Explain. Why is this not allowed
   by some teachers?

Sources for Alternative Teaching Strategies

Question 27: If your students are experiencing difficulty in understanding your development of a topic in mathematics, what are your sources of other strategies for teaching the topic?

Teacher Responses

(5) My school district has a math specialist who is available for consultation. She may make suggestions for a new approach or get materials together for me to try. *(Grade 1)*

(7) We have some filmstrips that have a different approach; sometimes, if one or two children seem to catch on when none of the others do, I will have them try to present it in a different light. Sometimes a different approach will be suggested in another textbook. *(Grade 5)*

(14) I have an extensive collection of commercial materials. I attend conferences and workshops whenever possible. I read and use the *Arithmetic Teacher* and other NCTM materials. I frequently draw upon this bank of information when having to develop alternate strategies. *(Grade 5)*

(47) I usually use manipulative materials so the students can physically see how the concept works. Another way is to have them talk through the problem verbally. This way I can see exactly where the difficulty lies. *(Grade 3)*

(65) The best resources are your fellow teachers. Don't be afraid to admit you can't get a concept across to your students. Nobody is perfect. *(Grade 6)*

(72) I use other textbooks from a lower grade level. These often have a simpler way of explaining concepts. *(Grade 5)*

Exercises for Question 27

1. List the sources that the respondents mention of other strategies for teaching a topic. Can you suggest additional sources? Which three sources would be most effective for you? Explain.

2. Have you had any experience in working with a K-8 or K-12 mathematics specialist? If so, in what way? How important is it for a school district to have a mathematics specialist? Explain.

3. Teacher 65 says that "The best resources are your fellow teachers." Are many teachers reluctant to seek teaching advice from other teachers? If so, why? What recommendations can you give for facilitating teacher discussion on teaching strategies?

4. **Project.** Using one or more of the sources suggested by the respondents, find three strategies for teaching second grade students how to find the answer to missing addend problems like $5 + ? = 9$.

Students' Making Up Work

Question 28: What provisions do you have for students' making up work that they have missed?

Teacher Responses

(2)   Because of the spiral development of our math program, a child can miss one or two weeks of school without too much difficulty in making up the work in math. Another child can help, and I can provide time during class periods when students are working on independent seatwork. *(Grade 1)*

(3)   Students are allowed to take their books home and make up any work they have missed. If they have missed the introduction of a new concept, then I have to find time to give them individual attention. *(Grades 4-5)*

(4)   Because of my individualized program, there is no need for make-up work unless a child is absent for a long time. A child upon returning just goes right on from where he or she left off. If the absence is rather long, a week or more, I send pages of maintenance work home with a note of explanation. If a child

begins a new module soon after returning from a long absence, I get the child started and when I see that the child understands the concept, then I send home reinforcement pages and aids just to move him or her along a little faster. *(Grade 1)*

(13) Work that students have missed while absent must be made up within a few days of returning to class. I often will dismiss or shorten the assignment if it has been review or if I am confident that the student can handle the material. It is ultimately the student's responsibility to turn in missing work. *(Grades 7-8)*

(17) If a student is to be absent for a number of days, many parents request a list of assignments. I suggest to the students who cannot understand the textbook explanation nor get help from their parents that they skip the difficult pages and go on to others. They then receive help upon returning to class without actually falling far behind. Parents of ill children often pick up assignments or request that they be sent home with a neighboring child. In other cases, the student is welcome to remain in during recess periods to catch up, or is given several days to catch up at home before being reminded that work is missing. *(Grade 6)*

(18) All assignments, quizzes, and tests are recorded daily on an assignment sheet that is posted on the bulletin board. Each student is responsible for checking that sheet (or one kept by another student in his or her notebook) for any make-up work. If the work is a reproducible page, quiz, or test that I would have, the student would need to see me. If any absence is for one or two days, the work is expected within the next day or two. If the absence is longer, we will devise a schedule. I expect students to be responsible by the time they get to this level. *(Grades 7-8)*

(25) Since most elementary math involves repetition, I do not insist that students make up *every* missing assignment. I find that the better students, while still absent from school, will find out what they missed and make it up. The poorer student will generally tackle the skill he or she missed upon returning to school. I watch them a little more closely as they work. I can measure whether or not they have the skill from that observation and the succeeding day's work. In the event of a lengthy absence, I will send work home with the student's brothers and sisters or parents. Usually, parents are cooperative and see that the child does the missing work. *(Grade 3)*

(28) It is the responsibility of the students who were absent to copy the notes from a fellow classmate for the days absent. They then see me for the assignment they must do. They can check their work with my answer book or with a classmate's notebook. *(Grades 7-8)*

(31) I keep a folder on my desk for each student. When a child is absent and I feel the child must make up the work, I put a paper stating the assignment in the child's class folder. Each child is required to check the folder when returning to class. Unless the child has been absent more than a day or two, it is the responsibility of the child to seek help if needed. When a child is absent for a longer period of time, I make certain that he or she receives help on any new concepts or skills that may have been presented while absent. *(Grade 4)*

(39) Students are asked to get other students' phone numbers at the beginning of the year. However, I let them know that they need their parents' permission to give out their phone number. I tell them that sometimes they may understand without my lecture and that they can ask another student about how to do the work. I stress that getting behind is more work than staying with the rest of the class. About ninety-five percent of my students take this advice. The only ones who do not are the chronic absentees. *(Grade 7)*

(42) In the case of an absence of one or two days, the student is expected to complete the worksheet that may have been assigned. In extended absences of two to three weeks, I may prepare special worksheets that explain the theory and contain completed sample problems followed by problems for the student to work. I discuss the first worksheet with the student as soon as he or she returns to school. The student may then work on this worksheet with a best friend or a fellow student who is capable of helping. *(Grades 5-6)*

Exercises for Question 28

1. Read the responses and then give your answer to Question 28. List the circumstances under which your students would not have to make up work that they have missed.

2. What time limits would you place on students for completing the work that they have missed? Explain.

3. What is or will be your policy on students' making up missed tests? Will you use the same test as that given to the class? Explain. What are the disadvantages of delaying for several days the return of a test until all students have taken it?

4. Teachers 18, 28, and 31 place certain responsibilities on the student for finding out about and making up missed work. What responsibilities do you or will you place on your students in this regard? Will you give reminders? What penalties will you assess if a responsibility is not met? Do your responses depend on grade level? Explain.

5. Suppose you have a student who is having difficulty with mathematics and you know that this student will be out of school for two weeks, but available for doing school work. What will you do for this student? (Be specific and thorough in your response.)

6. Suppose a student comes back to school after having missed several days of important mathematics. It may take this student several days to make up this work, and during this time suppose the class is continuing on with new ideas that require a knowlege of the previous work. Give a management plan for helping this student catch up with the class.

Techniques for Motivating Students

Question 29: What specific techniques do you use to motivate your students to learn mathematics?

Teacher Responses

(3) The students and I periodically take an objective look at their progress as a whole. We recall what mathematical skills they had when they entered the fourth grade. We talk about their newly acquired skills and areas of growth; then we look to the future and plan together, which includes a look ahead in the textbook. I have stated that my goal for them is to walk out that door on the last day of class in June feeling very optimistic and comfortable about entering the fifth grade math class. I believe most of my students have accepted that goal for themselves. They know that I have pledged to do all that I can to help them; they also know that to be successful they must participate and become involved. Sometimes we discuss how learning takes place. *(Grades 4-5)*

(4) I usually have no motivational problem with this age level. The manipulatives, the games, the gross-motor-acting-out activities all appeal to the children. Tying in math activities with

everyday life helps also. In the beginning of the year I do a booklet with the children called *Numbers Everywhere.* We illustrate almost thirty ways in which numbers are a part of their lives, such as their birthday, age, phone number, address, number in family, number of grade, room number in school, number of pages in textbook, height, weight, etc. They seem to enjoy this activity and learn from it. It helps with vocabulary development. *(Grade 1)*

(8)   Being able to work at their own pace is very motivating for many children. I enjoy math and I try to approach each new concept as a challenge that we can meet and master. All things are not easy but the work is worth the effort! The children enjoy the math centers because it seems less like work and more like fun, even though they are learning and reviewing math skills. *(Grades 3-4)*

(9)   Fortunately, I have never had much trouble motivating the children in math. Most of them love math and consider it their best subject. Having the students in appropriate skill groups insures success and helps motivate them. *(Grade 5)*

(11)   This is rather difficult to answer since I really don't set out to motivate. I think I just have high expectations of them, and they seem to rally around that. If the work load and difficulty level are appropriate for a student, motivation is usually possible to maintain in that student. However, I try to inject enthusiasm in my presentations and hope it becomes contagious. Also, when presenting a new math concept, I try to relate its mastery as prerequisite to learning a future math concept. *(Grade 3)*

(17)   Certainly no one technique works with all youngsters. Allowing students to go ahead at their own rate stimulates some to do more in class and at home. Those who are ahead are often granted independent math time in the media center, or extra computer time when other classes do not show up at their scheduled time. Equations Club membership, open to all fourth through sixth graders, has helped motivate some average math students to learn more about multiple operations, exponents, square and cube roots, use of parentheses, order of operations, substitute names for numerals, etc. I give rewards for accurate papers and for making corrections. A neat, well-organized paper from a student who has been handing in rather poor, difficult-to-check papers may get a reward and the following note, "A neat paper! Easy to read. Thanks for making my job easier, David." Every student has his or her own small section of bulletin board space. I suggest that they put up papers they are proud of for room visitors to see. Several students do this regularly, but more so during the first few months of the school year. I have teacher-made math posters on most of the available wall space in the classroom.

Some well-placed remarks to a non-listener sometimes help: "Say, Bob, you'd better not tell those math teachers at the junior high that you came from my room or this school. Make it the Bond School in Cherokee, Wyoming or some such place." Equally often a student may hear, "That's great. If someone asks where you learned that, say out loudly and clearly, 'Mrs. Smith at Garver School.'" I would like to think that my own interest in math is a motivating force. *(Grade 6)*

(18)   If nothing else motivates students, frequent quizzes and tests do, along with the daily recording of assignments. During most chapters, I use puzzles that give some kind of picture or message. I also use games and varied bulletin boards. Classroom discussion and humor are important, although I try to create a climate that still has structure and a time for quiet work. I try to generate a friendly, cheerful, yet relaxed atmosphere within the classrooom. *(Grades 7-8)*

(24)   I believe that the structure of my math program generates self-motivation, as does my enthusiasm for math in all content areas of learning. I use praise and self-evaluation at the close of each math class and peer compliments. I encourage students to be competitive with themselves, not with their peers. *(Grades 3-5)*

(25)   Motivation is not usually a significant problem at this level. Third graders still are enthusiastic about learning. I do impress upon them the importance of the four basic operations and try to point out the situations when they will need to use the process they are learning. I also impress upon them which skills they are reviewing and which are new skills that they will need for fourth grade. The idea of learning a new skill for the next grade--or of learning ahead of time a skill that is taught in fourth grade--is very important to them and serves as a great motivator. *(Grade 3)*

(26) My first goal is to be well prepared to teach each topic. I also try to be as interested in the material as I would like the students to be. I believe the best motivating factor in the classroom should be the teacher. *(Grade 8)*

(31) I run a contest to encourage the children to learn the basic facts. I also have them keep a bar graph showing the number correct on each quiz so they can see their progress. It is a bit more difficult to motivate the children on daily work. I will not allow them to get away with not handing in an assignment. Sometimes the follow through is very time-consuming for me, and sometimes involves writing notes or making calls to parents. However, I have found that most children soon get the idea that it is easier to do the work when it should be done, because they are going to have to deal with it sooner or later anyway. There is a bit of negative reinforcement here, but I have never found a way to totally avoid it. Besides, I definitely feel children need to learn that life contains many things we have to do, like it or not. *(Grade 4)*

(32) I relate new concepts to those already known by the student. I think through a problem with the students. When we get the answer I say, "See how easy that was" or "You knew the answer yourself but just didn't know how to write it." Mathematics is a game (like checkers, baseball, etc.). If you know the ten digits and the place-value concept (the Magic Ten) and practice skills (just like an athlete), you can play the game successfully and have fun. *(Grade 3)*

(37) I insist on their best possible attention as the first thing. I involve students as much as possible rather then lecture at them. Visual aids are used so as to employ the visual senses as an added incentive to learning. *(Grade 2)*

(41) I use clear expectations, monitor and follow up homework, hold conferences with parents, share with each student his or her State Assessment Test scores, and help students identify some of their math deficiencies. *(Grade 7)*

(42) My basic philosophy fits here: success breeds success. At the beginning of the year, I offer a money-back guarantee: if each student follows along, does what is asked, and memorizes certain material, I guarantee that all the students will succeed and like math. There are skeptics, but my approach has sufficient appeal to make them want to give it a whirl, and we start off with a positive attitude.

It troubles me greatly that children arrive pre-sorted in their own minds: Student A is good at math; Student B is not. I discuss this openly, assure them that they all are potentially good math students, and state that they will ultimately take another look at students now regarded as poor. Having done this for years, I never fail to get the one self-proclaimed victim I need. Usually a boy, he announces he does not like math and he'll *never* be good at it. He's the student who wants to say this about himself before someone else does. I merely respond with total confidence, "We're going to change all that, Larry." It sets the stage. I nurture my victim (as I do others) with much praise for minor successes and lots of positive support. Sooner or later, my victim turns in a perfect math paper at which time I ask the class, "Guess who turned in a perfect paper?" By now, they have forgotten the earlier scene and rattle off the names of the pre-determined "good" math students. After several attempts, I announce, "No, Larry did." Almost always this is met with a burst of genuine applause. It not only has a tremendous effect on Larry but on the others as well. An "If-Larry-can-do-it-so-can-I" attitude develops. This often starts a One Hundred Percent Club. Each competes with himself or herself, tries to upgrade accuracy, and strives for a perfect paper. It's at this time that I remind my students that I told them they would change their minds about who's good and who is not. The message is pretty clear: you may think of yourself as a poor math student, but that can be changed.

A pleasant atmosphere is essential. I do my utmost to provide lively (sometimes dramatic) presentations, completely devoid of pressure or stress. Humor, as a tool, is used constantly. In subtraction, we do not borrow, we *steal*, since we have no intention of paying it back. Several years ago in a discussion of place value with decimals, I stressed the importance of the decimal point by making one with a diameter of about two inches. Spontaneously, I added cat ears and a tail. The children immediately declared it should have a name and decided on Ralph. The concept stuck but I was stuck with Ralph. I'm convinced this kind of thing increases motivation and assists in retention. In the same vein I make up story problems using the children's names and ridiculous situations. For example, George has a new pet--a 16 foot, green and white spotted elephant. He's preparing a pen for it that is 35 feet long and 15 feet wide. How much fencing will he need? If he decided to cover the pen floor with purple shag carpet, how much will he need? They enjoy doing these problems. Whenever possible I put people into math. I use the history of math, e.g., the history of the development of place value and zero. One example of a multiplication problem done with Roman numerals and they're quite happy to go back to manipulating their ten little digits. I take every opportunity to increase self-confidence. If you believe, you can fly! *(Grades 5-6)*

(45) I always begin a lesson by telling students the reasons for which they need to know the material. I might tell a story, pose a problem involving the students, or give an overview of the ideas I plan to present. *(Grades 3-4)*

(55) There are a lot of interesting characters in the CSMP elementary school program that come up on a regular basis. There is Eli the elephant and his friend Clarence the crocodile. There is Mr. Booker and his bakery. There is Nora, her grandmother, and Nora's many friends. The list goes on and on. The children become very interested in this group of characters. They are always interested when I begin by saying "Let's see how Clarence is going to fool Eli today!" The class shows instant and genuine interest, like adults following the escapades of characters in the soaps. This is a built-in motivator. As the children become more mature and skillful, other motivators are introduced, such as the following: counting money and change to be able to shop, being able to divide for sharing purposes, and being able to find perimeter for practical reasons. In the manner of metaphors, the storybook characters open the door for the children and the practical life applications sustain their interest. *(Math Lab Teacher, Grades 1-5)*

(65) My techniques include the following activities:
1. Many winter holiday crafts involve measuring, cutting, and geometric shapes. We usually do a geometry unit near Christmas in which we make Santas, geometric ornaments, wreaths, etc.
2. Studying the metric system can be more fun if, for example, the linear measurements are done outside.
3. Combining math with other subject areas is fun. One year we measured off the size of the Mayflower ship on the

parking lot and then jammed it with the number of pilgrims that travelled on it. Quite a crowd!

4. Instead of always having paper and pencil activities, use colored chalk on the school sidewalks or parking lots. The kids love the change and it looks neat when it rains!

5. Estimating is always fun if time is taken to check the accuracy of the estimate. For example, have your students measure to see how many meters it is from the front door to the bus stop after they have approximated this distance.

I reward students with such things as an occasional food treat, certificates for mastery of specific skills, "Happy-Grams" to parents, and displays of successful work on a chart or bulletin board. Variety is my key to being a successful math teacher. Vary your approach. *(Grade 6)*

(71)   My methods of motivation include having my students' art, music, and physical education teachers incorporate a particular math skill in their programs. I reward students by giving verbal praise or high letter grades. *(Grade 3)*

(74)   The technique that I have developed over the past twenty years that has been highly stimulating and motivating for my students in the area of mathematics, as well as in other subject areas, is that of team competition. This technique must be kept finely tuned by the teacher in order to give true meaning to the word "competition." There must be group interaction, rewards, and penalties. *(Grade 6)*

Exercises for Question 29

1. Select four techniques for motivating students mentioned by the respondents that are particularly meaningful to you. Why did you choose these?

2. Give reasons why class discussion on mathematics (i.e., teacher-student and student-student interchange) can motivate the learning of mathematics. Which respondents to this question use this technique?

3. Comment on this statement: If you, as a mathematics teacher, are enthusiastic about helping your students learn mathematics, then you will be enthusiastic about mathematics and the teaching of it. Would Teacher 26 agree with this statement?

4. Can the giving of frequent quizzes and tests motivate the learning of mathematics? Explain. What effect will the late returning of quizzes and tests have on a student's motivation to learn mathematics? Explain. How late is "late" for returning tests and quizzes?

5. Is it motivating, as Teacher 24 suggests, for students to know that they should be competitive with themselves and not with their peers? Explain.

6. Teacher 4 says that motivation is generally not a problem for first graders and that this is due in part to the child's being actively involved in his or her learning. Do you agree with this? Explain. Do you think a more activity-based learning environment at the middle school level would be a significant motivating factor? Explain.

7. Teacher 31 speaks about negative reinforcement as a technique to motivate students to learn mathematics. What role should negative reinforcement play in motivation? Explain. What other types of negative reinforcement, not mentioned by Teacher 31, would you use? (For another suggestion, see Teacher 18.)

8. In the second paragraph of Teacher 42's response, she mentions the problem of motivating students who enter her classroom with a negative attitude about their ability to learn mathematics. What suggestions can you give, beyond those given by Teacher 42, to help these students overcome this attitude?

9. No respondent speaks explicitly to the different kinds of problems in motivating the slow learner in comparison to the fast learner. Do you think this distinction should be made? Explain. What are some motivational techniques particularly appropriate for the fast learner? The slow learner?

10. **Project.** Read the bulletin "Motivation in Mathematics," which appears in *Research Within Reach: Elementary School Mathematics* (1). Critique the section "Teacher-Student

Communication." Can you give additional ideas about how a teacher's knowledge of a specific student can provide a framework upon which to motivate the student?

11. **Project.** Methods of motivating students at the outset of a lesson include simply and clearly stating the goals of the lesson (see comments by Teachers 41 and 45), appealing to the students' interests (see comment by Teacher 45), and posing a problem with a solution that is not accessible at the outset of the class period but will be at the end. For each of these techniques, choose a specific mathematics lesson from a grade level textbook and illustrate how you would use the technique. (Attach copies of the textbook pages.)

Relating Math
to the Real World

Question 30:   How do you relate mathematics to the "real" world?

Teacher Responses

(2)   The teacher's edition of our textbook includes suggestions such as using open-ended stories that initiate class discussion and relate the mathematics to a six-year-old's real world. Students' responses to the open-ended stories vary considerably, which makes each lesson an exciting and challenging experience. *(Grade 1)*

(4)   When working with the concepts of addition, subtraction, and one-to-one correspondence, I try to use real world examples that involve setting the table, knocking down bowling pins, passing out supplies and treats at school, etc. We also do some cooking, count lockers, and talk about the calendar and clock. *(Grade 1)*

(8)   I try to incorporate as much math as I can in other subjects such as science and social studies. For example, each year we study a different country in depth. We use math to convert ethnic

recipes to the measures we need for cooking. We find out the exchange rate of currency and translate dollars into the money of that country. We look at maps and compare relative sizes and populations of our country and the one we're studying. We figure how long it would take to fly there given the distance and airplane speed. Math can be incorporated like this in most areas of study. *(Grades 3-4)*

(10) We have had children get paid play money for various jobs they do in the room. They have bank accounts and they have to pay money out of their accounts for paper, pencils, books, etc. They also learn how to write a check and balance their accounts. We also have a store in which the children can buy things and make change. *(Grades 3-4)*

(11) Having been on the Career Education Committee of our district, my research revealed that on an elementary level it's good to relate each school subject to the world of work as your students study the subject. For example, while we are on the measuring unit, we discuss its use by carpenters, by movers, in household situations, etc. Other math areas are related to the world of work in a similar way. *(Grade 3)*

(17) We have several activities that help relate mathematics to the real world. Some examples are: following the stock market for several weeks, school meter readings for purposes of conservation of energy and money, price comparing in newspaper ads, operation of the school supply store by a number of students in the class, several cooking activities, school-wide bake sale, weekly bagel sale, and class discussions of math-related careers. We also relate math to the computer. *(Grade 6)*

(33) Many of the articles in the *Scholastic Mathematics* magazine relate to the "real" world. We discuss and work out the exercises together as a class activity. *(Grade 6)*

(36) Many of the stories in the CSMP elementary school program involve life-like situations. Some of the stories encourage you to use the names of students in your class. I also use every real problem that naturally arises in class as a problem for my class to work on. For example, we have figured out by how many points Michigan's basketball team has won (or lost) to opposing teams. We've talked about the total cost for our class

to do something. We've figured how long it will be until recess or a special event. We have programmed the computer to count to a million and have approximated how long it would take an individual to do this. We have subtracted to find out how long ago an event in history occurred. We do calculations, which some of the children may or may not understand, whenever an opportunity presents itself. *(Grade 3)*

(42)   Sometimes we have major projects lasting two to three weeks and usually held at the very end of the year when students begin to lose interest. Once another teacher and I agreed to have a "business" activity for our classes. One class was divided into groups and each group created a store. The groups made placards bearing pictures of their products (from old catalogs) and prices of items. The groups were responsible for keeping their store records, and each student was responsible for balancing a personal checkbook (made from a reproducible master). The groups split profits from sales. The second class was the bank. Accounts were kept for stores and individual students. We used deposit and withdrawal slips, and bank statements were sent to customers. Bank employees earned a salary via bank fees. All students had an opportunity to shop, to visit the bank to transact business, and to do the computations for the day's activities.

For a one-class activity, children are paid for coming to school with each being given an hourly rate by lottery; from this they figure their daily and weekly salaries. Checkbooks are used to pay them each Monday morning. Certain students are identified as landlords, a utility company, or suppliers (of notebook papers, pencils, etc.). All students have to pay a percent of their weekly incomes (which they have to compute) for rent, utilities, etc. This is the core of the project. Other math concepts are easily added as well as social studies concepts. Once, the classroom was divided into four sections (high to low rent areas). High rent areas had distinct advantages. Discussions about this and their feelings made our community more real. This led to low income students requesting ways to increase income. A spontaneous incident may expand the project. Once, when the group was much too noisy, I declared myself to be the law enforcement agency and levied a fine on each student. One student, who felt he did not contribute to the melee (and therefore was unjustly fined), decided to sue me. This led to court cases complete with judge, prosecuting and defense attorneys, and witnesses. Naturally, all appropriate court costs were duly included. *(Grades 5-6)*

Exercises for Question 30

1. Teachers 2 and 4 are first grade teachers. Comment on the appropriateness of their suggestions for how to relate mathematics to the "real" world at that grade level. What additional suggestions can you give for this grade level?

2. Teachers 8, 10, 11, and 36 are third and fourth grade teachers. Comment on the appropriateness of their suggestions for how to relate mathematics to the real world at these grade levels. What additional suggestions can you give for these grade levels?

3. Teachers 17, 33, and 42 are fifth and sixth grade teachers. Comment on the appropriateness of their suggestions for how to relate mathematics to the real world at these grade levels. What additional suggestions can you give for these grade levels?

4. What does the phrase "real world problem" mean to you? Give reasons why it is important for teachers to give real world problems to their students.

5. Give reasons for students solving both of the following types of mathematical problems: real world problems stated in the textbook and real world problems that are constructed by the teacher and relate to the students' current experience. How often would you have the latter problems for your students? Explain.

6. What message is Teacher 8 giving her students by incorporating mathematics in most areas of their study? Are you or will you be doing this? Why isn't this done more often?

7. Critique the response of Teacher 42. Do the benefits outweigh the cost of the time given to such projects? Explain.

8. **Project.** Read the article "The Newspaper: A Source for Applications in Mathematics" by Francis Fennell in the October 1982 issue of the *Arithmetic Teacher*. Critique this article. Select a newspaper and construct three student activities for a specific grade level.

9. **Project (for K-6 teachers).** Read the article "Another Look at Applications in Elementary School Mathematics" by Wirtz and Kahn in the September 1982 issue of the *Arithmetic Teacher*. Give the basic ingredients of a presentation that you would make to your classmates or colleagues on the content of this article.

District's Policy on Length of Math Period

Question 31:   What is your district's policy on the length of the mathematics class period?

Teacher Responses

(1)   We are to have fifty minutes of mathematics five days a week. *(Grades 1-5)*

(4)   I asked my principal this question. He said that there is no school district policy on this but that about an hour per day is recommended. A colleague of mine heard him say this and she took issue with him, stating that it should be less. They then more or less agreed that the hour he recommended would include the more formal instructional time as well as the informal and incidental math-related games and activities during the day. *(Grade 1)*

(24)   The policy is forty-five minutes per day. Much more time than this is used since math is integrated into all learning. *(Grades 3-5)*

(33) In the middle school (sixth through eighth grades) the mathematics class is a fifty-five minute period. *(Grade 6)*

(37) One hour per day is required for the CSMP elementary school program. *(Grade 2)*

(39) We have fifty-minute periods but I do some math work in science classes if appropriate (e.g., metric system). *(Grade 7)*

(51) There is no set policy for the elementary school. Most teachers tend to have from forty to sixty minutes. *(Grades 2-3)*

(52) The district recommends from fifty to sixty minutes for fourth through sixth grades and from thirty to forty minutes for kindergarten through third grade. *(Grades 4-5)*

Exercises for Question 31

1. Should a school district have a stated policy on the length of the mathematics class period? If yes, explain why. If no, who should determine the length?

2. Three possible policies for the time devoted to mathematics instruction are: 250 minutes per week, 50 minutes per day, and 45 to 55 minutes per day. Which policy do you prefer? Explain.

3. **Project.** Determine what your State Board of Education says about the minimum length of the mathematics class period or about the minimum number of minutes per week that must be in the mathematics program.

Time of Class Period

Question 32: Give your weekly mathematics time schedule. At what time of day is your mathematics class period, and if you had your choice, when would you hold it?

Teacher Responses

(4) On two days of the week the math class period is from 8:45 to 9:30 A.M. and on the remaining three days it is held from 12:30 to 1:15 P.M. The reason for these different times is that I choose to alternate reading and math; this works very well. *(Grade 1)*

(9) I generally have math in the afternoon, which I prefer because a larger block of time is available then to do the math work. My mornings are broken up with band, glee club, special classes, scheduled reading, etc. *(Grade 5)*

(20) I devote one hour to math daily. I usually hold it the first thing in the morning from 9:30 to 10:30. If it conflicts with gym, art, or music, we have it the first thing in the afternoon. I prefer the first thing in the morning. *(Grade 4)*

(22) If math classes are conducted in the first period after lunch during the first semester, I then reverse the math period in the second semester to the first morning period. This allows for the "morning people" and the "afternoon people" to have a time in the school year for math when they are operating at their prime time. *(Grade 6)*

(24) On Mondays, Thursdays, and Fridays I have math from 2:30 to 3:25. On Tuesdays and Wednesdays, it's from 1:00 to 2:00. Right after lunch was the students' preference for math, but they were willing to make the adjustment to having it the last period of the day so high school student aides could be with us. Additional class time is used throughout the day for problem solving, special math work, and resource people. I think any time of day would be fine for math. Students often work on math other than during the math period. They often complain when class is over, or state, "Time went by so fast." You will often see them in the room before school begins working on math. *(Grades 3-5)*

(32) My math class is from approximately 10:45 to 11:40 each day of the week. Whether teaching third, fourth, or sixth grade, I have always taught math the last thing each morning. Students are most alert at this time and they also get a break from all the word-oriented subjects. *(Grade 3)*

(45) Since I am a speciality teacher I have four math classes each day, five days per week, with fifty minutes per period. The time of day really does not matter if interest is high and the teacher knows what he or she is presenting and how to do it. *(Grades 3-4)*

Exercises for Question 32

1. Suppose you, as a teacher, have the freedom to determine when your mathematics class period should be scheduled. What matters should you consider when making this decision, and why are they important to consider?

2. How much freedom should the classroom teacher have in deciding the time of the day for the mathematics class period? Explain.

3. Should the classroom teacher have the right to insist that, in general, individual students not be interfered with by persons outside the classroom during the mathematics class period? Explain.

4. Teachers 4, 20, 22, and 24 change the time during the week or year when they schedule their mathematics class period, and they do this for different reasons. Critique each of their schedules.

5. Teachers 24 and 45 think, from the standpoint of student performance, that it does not make any difference as to the time of day that the mathematics class period is held. Teachers 22 and 32 think that it does make a difference. What do you think? Explain.

Allotting Class Time

Question 33:   Describe how the class time is allotted to the various aspects of your mathematics lesson.

Teacher Responses

(5)   If there is a new skill to be introduced, I spend approximately thirty minutes on instruction and group practice with manipulatives. The last fifteen minutes is used for written practice. *(Grade 1)*

(10)   We often begin class by checking our assignment from the day before. The children then have to correct their mistakes. I explain the new assignment, which usually takes ten to twenty minutes. If it's a new concept, I often have children work problems on the board for about ten to fifteen minutes. They then do their assignment for about a half hour. *(Grades 3-4)*

(18)   The first five minutes are devoted to attendance and other business matters, followed by five to twenty minutes checking and discussing the previous day's assignment and returning old assignments, followed by fifteen to twenty minutes on discussion of new materials, and finally, from zero to fifteen

minutes for homework, with any incomplete assignments to be finished at home. *(Grades 7-8)*

(20)   The one hour of math is divided as follows: ten minutes of drill on computational facts, twenty to twenty-five minutes on board instruction or hands-on and oral experiences, and fifteen to twenty-five minutes on seatwork. When and if time permits, students work on games or activity cards. *(Grade 4)*

(25)   The morning allotment time of twenty minutes is the approximate time it takes the students to do two worksheets in their seatwork packet, one on review and the other on the current skill for that week. This time does not include an instruction time of five minutes or less. The afternoon allotment time of thirty-five minutes is used for text instruction. The first ten minutes or so is used to introduce the skill for that day, and the remainder of the time is for the students to work on the assignment. *(Grade 3)*

(36)   Approximately five to ten minutes is used for oral or written math facts drill, twenty-five minutes for instruction, and twenty-five minutes for pencil and paper applications or other responses. Our CSMP elementary school program often mixes instruction with the actual work that the children do so time allotments do not fall into discrete segments. *(Grade 3)*

Exercises for Question 33

1.   Make a chart that gives for each respondent the daily allotment of time to these aspects of the mathematics lesson: (a) previous day's assignment, (b) developmental work, and (c) working on the new assignment. Which respondent's class time allotment do you most agree with? Explain. Which respondent's class time allotment do you least agree with? Explain. How would you complete the chart for a grade level of your choice?

2.   Under what circumstances would you devote the whole class period to developing the new lesson? To going over yesterday's assignment? To reviewing previous material?

3. How important is it for a teacher to insure that his or her students can work problems in class that are related to a new assignment, called controlled practice, before they work independently on the assignment? Explain.

4. How important is it to schedule time in your mathematics class for oral work? Explain. What are appropriate times for doing oral work?

Miscellaneous Comments on Math Teaching

Question 34: Are there any other comments on mathematics teaching you would like to make that will help attain the objectives of this questionnaire?

Teacher Responses

(16) The teaching of mathematics, like any subject, requires that the teacher know the students. There is more to teaching than simply presenting material. What works for one child may not work for another. Do not lose sight of the individual. *(Grade 6)*

(21) I feel that next to reading, math is the most important subject in school. Children who have a good math background in the early years have a better chance to feel good about math throughout their whole education. Being an early grade teacher, I see how important it is that children know, really know, their math facts by memory. They can complete other tasks with ease when they have the facts committed to memory. Math can be fun! And that is a fact children need to learn early in their schooling years. *(Grade 2)*

(22) The larger the class, the more math deficiencies will be found and the more difficult it will be to remedy these deficiencies. *(Grade 6)*

(36) Mathematics in the elementary school should be presented by teachers who like math and who teach a concept before asking students to work problems. Those who over-stress the working of problems, at the expense of good developmental work, think that every answer must be arrived at by a specific method, usually by their method, whatever that happens to be. These people are intimidated by problems that don't have answers in the teacher's manual and by children who find a different way to solve a problem. It may eventually be necessary to have a math specialist who teaches all the math in grades four to six. Some elementary school teachers do not have the math background necessary to teach mathematics. These people are unsure of themselves, are often intimidated, and convey these feelings to their students. *(Grade 3)*

(40) All too often the math program in elementary classrooms consists of handing the child a book and letting the child work at his or her own level. There is little group instruction, mental math, creative problem solving, or verbalization of concepts. Another problem is that many textbooks need a lot of supplementing. True, teachers can hunt up various resources to supplement the text, but a more successful program would be one in which the teacher's manual is full of easy to use and interesting activities that help develop all the concepts. The CSMP elementary school program I use has one of the best manuals I have ever used. The teacher definitely makes the difference in implementing any program, but her life can be made much easier if there are many ideas at her fingertips and the program is good to begin with. *(Grade 2)*

(43) Some of my comments are: students must feel comfortable in class so that they will ask questions when the subject matter is unclear; students should be allowed to work together sometimes, but individual effort must be promoted; a coordination of subject matter is important (e.g., spelling of mathematical terms, handwriting, and applications of math skills to home economics and science); and students have to assume responsibility for their own development and cannot be constantly led by the teacher--the goal of the teacher should be to make oneself unneeded. *(Grade 8)*

(44) I am a big fan of the CSMP elementary school progam. If properly trained (twenty-five hours), any homeroom teacher can use the CSMP program. Problem solving and forgotten areas such as geometry and probability are covered in this program. The three non-verbal languages help a teacher involve a student, regardless of his or her reading level, in logical thinking and problem solving.

Emphasis on standardized tests, or at the very least the content of these tests, has to change. As long as administrators are rated according to certain scores on tests, they will put pressure on teachers to reach these scores regardless of what is sacrificed to do it. You will have a fantastic curriculum that teaches how to pass certain standardized tests, but I don't know how much math will be learned.

Finally, we must view students for what they are. Many are hard-working, bright, sensitive people. Others are not. We as teachers must effect their affective education. Do not allow students to laugh at another student's wrong answer. Each student must be impressed with the idea that we must respect and be sensitive to other people's worth and feelings. Encourage students to answer regardless of whether the response is right or wrong. Emphasize the importance of trying to figure out problems, and that many times we learn more from our mistakes than from the correct answers. Also stress that if we never made mistakes, we wouldn't need to be in school as there would be nothing to learn. It is through involvement that we learn. *(Grades 1-5)*

(45) I firmly believe that an effective mathematics teacher is well trained and familiar with the current literature in the field; that school boards, regions, and districts should make available meaningful refresher courses, workshops, educators' days, etc.; and that perhaps once a semester a school day can be used for a mathematics field day for examining new materials or for hearing speakers discuss new trends, directions, and ideas. *(Grades 3-4)*

(50) One of the most useful techniques I've found for teaching a lesson and ensuring instant feedback is the use of "think pads" or "scratch pads." Each student has a pad. When a lesson is being presented and they are working on a problem, they hold up their pads when done and I have a clear view of how the lesson is going. I use this technique for all subjects. *(Grades 4-5)*

(52) In addition to the traditional program that I've tried to cover in this questionnaire, I'm also involved with the CSMP elementary school program. It is a program that turns kids on more than any program I've ever tried. The main emphasis is on problem solving and teaching children that math can be fun. There is computation involved in the program at all levels, but the formal algorithms are delayed a bit longer than in a traditional program. *(Grades 4-5)*

(69) As a college, high school, and grade school student, I hated, despised, and dreaded math. I only took one course in college and the minimum in high school. Before I taught I feared teaching math in the classroom! Now I enjoy teaching math more than any other subject. I really plan hard for math and put much effort into teaching it. It's so much fun! *(Grade 3)*

(71) Don't worry about everything that comes your way. If you're not keeping up with other teachers at your grade level, so what. Their class may be smarter than yours (really). Even though you, and other teachers, expect to get a haphazard mixture of munchkins each September, certain classes seem to contain most of the brains. Once you have your class, stress neatness early in the year. Don't let the kids turn in messy work. Of course, from some, it may be wise to take chicken scratches because it's that or nothing. Realize that no matter what you do, some kids won't learn much because they don't care. Do what you can, but at times you have to get away from their learning problems. You have to keep a sense of humor. *(Grade 3)*

(77) Teachers, help children delight in mathematics. Take time to comprehend what a delight it can be! *(Grade 3)*

(79) My goal is to increase students' ability to produce ideas. It is not good work when they do what I tell them to do or when they please me. It is good work when they meet their own expectations. My job is to keep these expectations high and relevant to the world in which they live and in which they will live. I cannot predict the skills they will need, but I can help prepare them to achieve these skills. *(Grade 8)*

Exercises for Question 34

1. What general comments would you like to make on the teaching of mathematics that may be of value to a mathematics teacher?

2. What are some of the inherent difficulties in teaching mathematics?

3. Give specific suggestions on what school districts can do to strengthen the mathematics skills and the mathematics teaching skills of their teachers.

4. Teacher 16 states that "The teaching of mathematics, like any subject, requires that the teacher know the students." What information about a student would be valuable to have and how can it be obtained?

5. Teacher 36 states that "It may eventually be necessary to have a math specialist who teaches all the math in grades four to six." Give the advantages and disadvantages of having this. Are you for or against this?

6. Teacher 40 comments on what mathematics programs in elementary classrooms all too often consist of. What is your perspective on what is generally happening in today's elementary mathematics classroom?

7. Teacher 44 infers that standardized tests "drive" the curriculum. Is this your impression? Explain. How can teachers resist the pressure to focus too much on preparing students to do well on such tests, thus slighting other elements of a sound mathematics program?

8. **Project.** Read the article "Teacher Effectiveness in the Elementary School" by Thomas L. Good in the *Journal of Teacher Education,* March-April 1979. What impact will this article have on your teaching of mathematics?

9. **Project.** Read the article "A Process-Product Study in Fourth-Grade Mathematics Classrooms" by Good and Grouws in the *Journal of Teacher Education,* May-June 1977. Give three characteristics of effective teaching mentioned in the article that particularly impressed you and mention why you were impressed.

10. **Project.** Read the article "Results and Implications of the Second NAEP Mathematics Assessment: Elementary School" by Carpenter et al. in the April 1980 issue of the *Arithmetic Teacher*. What is this article saying to you as a teacher of mathematics?

11. **Project.** A particularly informative paperback on mathematics anxiety is *Mind Over Math* by Kegelman and Warren, published by McGraw-Hill Book Company, 1978. We highly recommend this book to both preservice and inservice teachers.

Annotated Bibliography of Selected Teacher Resources and Classroom Materials

1. *Research Within Reach: Elementary School Mathematics* by Mark Driscoll. Reston, Va.: National Council of Teachers of Mathematics, 1981.

   This is an excellent resource for the classroom teacher, discussing what research has to say about mathematics instruction in grades K–8. This booklet can be obtained through the NCTM (2) or from Dale Seymour Publications (6).

2. **National Council of Teachers of Mathematics (NCTM).** 1906 Association Drive, Reston, VA 22091.

   This is the professional organization for teachers of mathematics. Membership includes a subscription to either of two journals (see below), as well as a 20 percent discount on their extensive list of educational materials. We recommend membership in this professional society. A membership application form and an annotated list of their educational materials can be obtained by writing to the address given above. We especially want to call your attention to the following NCTM teacher resource materials.

   Journals. The NCTM offers two journals, one for elementary and one for secondary teachers. Each is a forum for the exchange of ideas and a source of techniques for teaching mathematics. They are as follows:
   Arithmetic Teacher (for grades K–8)
   Mathematics Teacher (for grades 7–12)

Of special interest are the following theme issues of the *Arithmetic Teacher:*

Comprehensive Curriculum (February 1979)
Assessing Student Learning (November 1979)
Mathematically Able Student (February 1981)
Teaching Problem Solving (February 1982)
Teaching with Microcomputers (February 1983)
Rational Numbers (February 1984)
Mathematical Thinking (February 1985)

Yearbooks. Each year the NCTM produces a yearbook, which is a compilation of articles by many authors. Recent yearbooks of particular interest are as follows:

Mathematics Learning in Early Childhood (37th Yearbook, 1975)
Developing Computational Skills (1978 Yearbook)
Problem Solving in School Mathematics (1980 Yearbook)
Teaching Statistics and Probability (1981 Yearbook)
Mathematics for the Middle Grades (5–9) (1982 Yearbook)
The Agenda in Action (1983 Yearbook)
Computers in Mathematics Education (1984 Yearbook)

An Agenda for Action: Recommendations for School Mathematics of the 1980s (1980).

The message of this booklet is critically important to teachers and school administrators in their current efforts to meet the needs of students in mathematics. Included are eight recommendations on such topics as the role of problem solving in school mathematics, an expanded definition of basic skills, and the place of calculators and microcomputers in mathematics instruction.

3. **Comprehensive School Mathematics Program (CSMP)**. Midcontinent Research Education Laboratory (McREL), 470 North Kirkwood Road, Second Floor South, St. Louis, MO 63122.

Many of the respondents in our book refer to this program. CSMP describes itself as a complete mathematics program, from basics to problem solving, for students of all ability levels in grades K–6, with content essential for understanding the nature of mathematics and its ever-increasing applications to diverse situations in the real world. The CSMP K–6 curriculum is part of the National Diffusion Network and has been approved as an exemplary program by the Joint Dissemination and Review Panel of the National Institute of Education and the U.S. Office of Education. Information and sample packets can be obtained by writing to the Director, CSMP at the address given above.

4. Mathematics Resource Project. University of Oregon (1977).

This is an extensive set of materials for grades 5–9, developed under a grant from the National Science Foundation. There are five resource packets: *Number Sense and Arithmetic Skills*; *Ratio, Proportion and Scaling*; *Geometry and Visualization*; *Mathematics in Science and Society*; *Statistics and Information Organization*. Each contains hundreds of pages of reproducible materials, including worksheets, calculator activities, games, puzzles, bulletin board suggestions, and project ideas. The entire collection provides practice with all the basic skills, including problem solving, mental computation, estimation, and measurement. Each resource packet includes teacher commentary and "didactics papers" that address key issues of mathematics instruction. These materials can be obtained from Creative Publications (6).

5. Problem Solving in Mathematics. The Lane County Mathematics Project (1983).

This program develops problem-solving skills in grades 4–9. There is one book for each grade level (grade 9 focuses on algebra), an alternative book for low achievers in grades 4–6, and an inservice guide. The suggested activities are to be integrated with the regular curriculum materials; by one plan, a teacher can develop one problem-solving skill each week for five weeks simply by taking about ten minutes of instruction time at the beginning of the mathematics period. The materials correlate well to the usual curriculum topics; many of the lessons can be used either to supplement or to replace textbook pages. Thus, problem-solving skills are enhanced and practiced throughout the school year. These materials can be obtained from Dale Seymour Publications (6).

6. Resource materials catalogs.

There are many sources for K–8 educational materials. We mention the following commercial sources because both have extensive collections of mathematics materials, some of which are referenced in the teacher responses in this book and elsewhere in this list of selected resources. Their catalogs can be obtained free upon request.

Dale Seymour Publications, P.O. Box 10888, Palo Alto, CA 94303.
Creative Publications, P.O. Box 10328, Palo Alto, CA 94303.